The Spectaculars

Gene Klinger

Reilly & Lee Books

A Division of Henry Regnery Company

To Kelli
May she
know them
well

Copyright © 1971 by Gene Klinger
All rights reserved.
Published 1971 by Reilly & Lee Books
A division of Henry Regnery Company
114 West Illinois Street, Chicago, Illinois 60610
Library of Congress Catalog Card Number 75-163273
Manufactured in the United States of America

Contents

The Spectaculars

THESE ARE the stories of the Greatest Showmen on Earth. That's what the posters and pitchmen called them And that's what they were—stage-struck jokers, "miracle" makers, and circus kings. Each was unique. Each was the very best of his kind.

Some were unequaled masters of magic and illusion, who held their audiences spellbound whenever they performed. Others were men in love with the laughter and lights of the circus, who gave their lives to make the Big Show bigger and brighter than it ever had been before. Wherever these showmen went, crowds followed and tried to imitate them. But none could ever be quite like the Spectaculars.

Long before the shadowy glow of a television screen brought laughter and adventure into everyone's living room, these men brought their special kind of magic to towns and sleepy hamlets everywhere. For them, life was a jumble of suitcases and trunks, hasty curtain calls and midnight travels to yet another town, another show. For them, there was only today—and tomorrow. This show. And the next.

Few who stared in wonder at these heroes' antics ever paused to consider the years of practice, determination, and courage that went into every performance. They were so good, these Spectaculars, that they made everything they did seem effortless. Their tricks were not easy, of course. But whoever saw a great magician whose hands shook or noticed the sweat on the forehead of a brightly painted clown?

On and on the Spectaculars went, sharing their world of one-night stands and make-believe. They were trying to make yesterday's magic even more wonderful today. And they were always, despite occasionally empty houses and empty pockets, incurable optimists. They came and were themselves, and always the night was more exciting and wondrous because they had appeared.

Grock was one of the funniest and most famous clowns the world has ever known. Audiences in Vienna and Paris, in Amsterdam and in cities all over the world laughed with and loved the bald, round-faced character who took an ordinary chair or fiddle —or any other commonplace object—and turned it into something strange and wonderful before their startled eyes. One day an admirer asked Grock why, since he could obviously have been anything at all, he had become a clown. "Because," Grock laughed, "I wanted to." This is how it happened.

Grock

"Adrien!"

Adrien jumped. He had been staring at the sugar bowl and imagining that he could hear it begging him to change it into something else. "Anything else," he had thought he heard the china bowl whisper, "anything except something as unexciting as I am now."

"Adrien!"

The startled boy looked up at his father. Adrien could tell from the tone of his voice that this was not the first or the second time that his father had spoken to him and he had not answered.

"Yes, sir." Adrien was surprised to find that he was not alone at the table, as he had imagined himself to be.

"How old are you now?"

"How old, Father?"

"Yes." Adrien's father paused and peered at him, questioningly, over the rim of his glasses. "This is 1895. You turned fifteen this year, didn't you?"

"Yes," Adrien replied. He watched his father stir his spoon around and around in his cup of tea. The spoon,

3

Adrien thought to himself, would be happier as a sea monster, an enormous sea monster stretching its long neck out of the dark brown water as it swam about in circles and . . .

"Adrien!"

Again the boy jumped. It wasn't so much his father's voice that startled him. But the sugar bowl, he had thought, had begun to turn into a giant whale, and Adrien had almost forgotten again that his father was there.

"Yes, Father?" he answered.

"As I was saying a moment ago, now that you're fifteen, I suppose you've given some thought to what you will do."

"Do?" Adrien asked, puzzled.

"When you grow up, Adrien. I imagine you've thought about what you will become."

"Yes. Uh, no. I mean, I have thought about it a great deal . . . but then, no, Father, I haven't decided."

Adrien squinted and stared again at the sugar bowl in front of him. "Perhaps," he said, "I'll take pictures."

"A photographer," his father replied, sounding pleased.

"Perhaps. Or maybe I'll pull teeth." Adrien bit his lower lip and frowned. "Molars, mostly," he mused.

"A dentist!" Adrien's father laughed at the thought.

"Or build boats," the boy said, smiling. "Or trim gardens. Or drive a horse and buggy."

"All those occupations . . . do you think they would make you happy?" Adrien's father asked.

Adrien was silent for what seemed like a long time. "No," he finally answered. "What will make me happy will be to do something . . . something spectacular. Something that makes people laugh. Something that will make them laugh harder than they've ever laughed before. That's what I want to do."

Adrien's father spoke to him, but the boy did not hear. Once again, he was busily staring at the sugar bowl, which suddenly seemed to him to be turning itself into a huge and very humorous walrus.

At fifteen, Adrien Wettach had little idea of what he wanted to do with his life, and even less of what he would actually come to be. There were so many different things that Adrien wanted to do then that he could not even begin to count them all, let alone choose among them. Each day seemed to cry out for him to take it and turn it into something new and exciting. And that is exactly what Adrien did.

If Adrien could have looked into the future and seen himself as a grownup, he would not have recognized himself. But he would have laughed—uproariously. He would have laughed at his pink, round face and roared at his bald head, as hairless and round as a billiard ball. And the red, bulbous nose, he would have found that funny, too. He would even have laughed at his new name, a name that was destined to make the whole world laugh with him: Grock. Grock, the famous clown who made the whole world seem wonderful and funny.

Grock's unpredictable, crazy way of seeing the world was something that, like his restless search for adventure, he had inherited from his father. Adrien had often been told how, as a boy, his father had vanished one day, only to be discovered several hours later among the performers in a traveling circus appearing in the next town.

Adrien knew that even as a grownup his father occasionally gave in to his love of adventure. Hadn't

Adrien's grandmother told him how, not too many years earlier, his father had fallen into the habit of disappearing each evening just before dinner? Night after night he vanished, never reappearing until long after dinner had turned cold and the fire in the hearth had gone out.

Adrien's mother became more and more worried. But she was a quiet woman who never said a word about her worries.

Then, one afternoon, a gossipy neighbor took the boy's mother aside. "If you want to see something that will make your hair stand on end," she whispered, shaking a bony finger at Mrs. Wettach, "go to the circus in Tavannes."

Adrien's mother stared in amazement at the old lady. She thought of Tavannes, the biggest village in the whole Swiss valley, and wondered what could be so exciting about the circus there.

"What could I possibly see," she asked, "that would be worth such a journey?"

The town gossip smiled a crooked smile. "Your husband," she answered. And then she turned and darted into one of the village's small shops.

Her husband? Adrien's father? Mrs. Wettach wondered what the old crow was talking about. Reaching into her worn apron pocket, she took what few coins she found and bought a train ticket to Tavannes.

The wooden train was rickety and noisy and slower, Adrien's mother thought, than anything she had ever ridden before. When the small engine and short string of cars finally crept to a halt in front of the frame station with the large sign lettered *Tavannes,* Mrs. Wettach was the first person to step off the train.

In the distance she could see the circus tent, and even over the noise of the gasping engine, she heard the roar of the crowd. A few minutes later, Adrien's mother was inside the tent and had found an unclaimed seat in the front row.

She hadn't found her seat too soon. Just then the band signaled the beginning of another act. As Mrs. Wettach sat down, the ring suddenly sparkled in the brightness of a single spotlight.

"Ladies and gentlemen!" the ringmaster called out in a voice that carried to the very last row. "Tonight you are about to witness a sight so rare, a sight so daring and death-defyingly dangerous, that you've never seen anything like it before in your lives!"

As Adrien's mother listened to the ringmaster, something she glimpsed out of the corner of one eye caught her attention. She tilted her head back as the spotlight moved upward, and her eyes followed it higher and higher to the point where a trapeze swung at the very top of the tent. Adrien's mother never took her eyes off that spot, for there she saw her husband swinging back and forth on the narrow trapeze!

At first she thought she would scream. But she did not dare to make a sound.

Mrs. Wettach stared in frozen silence as her husband swung back and forth in higher and higher arcs. She watched, hands clapped over her mouth, while he swung from the trapeze and was caught by another aerialist. Again and again he swung through the air. And each time, seemingly at the very last second, he was caught by his partner.

Adrien's mother only held her breath when her husband stepped onto a narrow platform high above the audience. But when he stepped out again and balanced tipsily on a thin strand of tightrope, she gasped.

It was not until the frightening performance was over and the familiar figure in the strange red tights was safely back on the ground that Mrs. Wettach called to her husband. He heard her voice and turned, his face as red as his costume. That night the circus's new daredevil aerialist left the ring, never to return again.

But Adrien's father never got over his restlessness. He and his family seemed always to be scurrying from place to place. In each new village, Adrien's father would find work repairing watches or managing a cafe. Their constant moving became the family's favorite joke. They were so robust, they would tell themselves laughingly, that they needed lots of fresh air. They needed so much air, they would laugh, that every few years they had to move to another village and another new sky—*full* of fresh air.

Wherever the family moved, Adrien quickly set about exploring his new surroundings. Ignoring the sidewalks and the streets, he would scurry along the tops of narrow railings and the fences surrounding public parks and gardens. Once he walked for more than half a mile without ever once setting foot on the ground.

By the time Adrien was old enough for school, he could walk the entire way atop the thin wire fences that lined the small gardens along the river's edge. After school, Adrien practiced walking the tightrope his father had stretched between two poles in their backyard. After a month of practice, he could walk it forwards and backwards. He even learned to turn about and jump on the thin rope without losing his balance.

Adrien's father raised the rope higher and higher, until finally it swung more than six feet above the ground.

One morning on his way to school, Adrien rounded the corner of a garden wall to discover the small village square filled with the splendid confusion of a traveling circus. Never before had he seen such a sight.

A pair of dust-covered circus wagons, their doors open wide and their window curtains blowing in the early morning breeze, were drawn up at one side of the square. Skinny horses chewed at the short grass. Several men, their shirts open to the breeze, busied themselves driving tent pegs into the ground; others worked together putting up a booth.

Somehow Adrien pulled himself away from this wondrous sight and continued on his way to school. He arrived on time, but all morning his thoughts lingered back in the village square. He pictured burly circus workers setting up the canvas between the tall tent poles and the head aerialist gingerly testing the high wire.

The schoolteacher, too, was well aware of the invaders who had crept into his village under the cover of night. When he looked about his classroom that morning, all he saw were empty, absentminded faces. His pupils were far away in another world, their lessons forgotten. At last noon came. The teacher reluctantly announced that the children would not have to hurry back to class that afternoon. "There will be no more school today," he said. Pointing an accusing finger in the direction of the village square, he told his class to "go, get the circus out of your blood, and be back ready to work in the morning!"

Outside, a breeze tugged at the trees and pulled at Adrien's shirttail. Never before had it felt so good to rush from the schoolhouse door and along the tops of the walls and fences. Never before had the old village square been transformed into such a wildly colorful and fantastic world all its own. Adrien lost himself in the wonders of this new world until long after dark.

The last rays of sunlight mixed with the glare of the naphtha lamps that flickered across the brightly colored costumes of the circus performers, who stood proudly in front of their tent. There were quick, agile acrobats. A roly-poly man with a chalk-white face and red, bulbous nose was the first clown Adrien had ever seen. He was someone Adrien would never forget.

It was quite late that evening when Adrien felt a hand on his shoulder and turned to see his mother, who had come once more to bring one of her men home from the enchantment of the circus. Adrien went home with her, and he took the memory of the roly-poly man with the clown face with him.

Again and again the Wettach family moved. One day they found themselves in Biel, a small town close to Switzerland's borders. In Biel everyone spoke German and French. Eleven-year-old Adrien discovered that the town was the meeting place for all sorts of wonderful wandering folk. Biel was the home of those mysterious souls who came out of nowhere bringing merry-go-rounds to carnivals—only to slip away again in the darkness once the fair's bright lights were dimmed. Brightly dressed, bearded proprietors of traveling waxworks, gypsy carnival bosses, and vagabond owners of shooting booths all called Biel their home.

The town's atmosphere and its colorful citizenry appealed to the Wettachs. Adrien's father opened a cafe, where the lad often watched magicians practicing their tricks. Adrien would stare, wide-eyed, then hurry to try the magic tricks himself. Never before had he been so excited—nor had he felt so much at home.

The Wettachs stayed in Biel for several years, much to Adrien's delight. As a teen-ager, he spent an increasing amount of time in his father's cafe. He was particularly fascinated with one of the customers—a clown who played tunes on bottles filled with varying amounts of colorful liquids. He resolved to learn how to play the bottles himself.

"Adrien, please," his mother would beg, "won't you practice the violin, instead? You could be a concert artist if you tried. Why must you waste your time on those silly bottles?"

But Adrien persisted until he had mastered and improved upon all the clown's tunes.

One night, when he was sixteen, Adrien had spent most of the evening at his father's cafe, cleaning tables and polishing glasses. All the time his eyes had been on the colorful customers and his ears tuned to their adventurous tales. He was so intent on a conversation between two customers—a juggler and a knife thrower—that he barely heard his father call.

"Adrien, come here, please."

The lad looked up quickly. Across the room he saw his father sitting with one of his guests at a small table. Putting down his towel and a half-polished glass, Adrien hurried across the crowded room.

"Adrien," his father smiled, "do you know Mr. Bourquin?"

Adrien nodded. Of course he knew Louis Bourquin. Hadn't everyone in Biel heard of the famous athlete and tightrope walker?

"Sit down, Adrien. Mr. Bourquin would like to have a few words with you. He's heard about your talent with the violin," his father laughed. "And with the little musical bottles of colored water, too."

Pulling his chair close to the table, Adrien stared at the man who sat across from him. "I understand that you are quite a good musician," the man said, his eyes twinkling.

Adrien shifted nervously in his chair.

"How would you like to perform in public?" Bourquin continued. "Before a *real* audience. A large audience. Practically everyone in Biel."

The lad stared across the table in silence. He could not believe that he had actually heard the words that were racing through his mind.

"Well, Adrien, what do you say?" Bourquin asked, chuckling at the lad's incredulity.

Adrien looked at his father. His father was laughing, too. He knew the excitement Adrien felt inside.

"Your father and I have talked over the whole matter," Bourquin explained. "He agrees that it would be good for you. Let me tell you my proposal. I'm going to walk a tightrope stretched across the square. While I do, and while hundreds of people stare in wonder at us from down in the streets below, *you,* Adrien, will play your music on the balcony alongside me."

The famous Mr. Bourquin looked at Adrien. Could he see—or hear—how fast the lad's heart was pounding?

"Everyone will hear your music, Adrien. They'll be stirred by it just as they'll be stirred by the sight of me walking that thin wire. And you'll be paid. Twenty francs, Adrien. What do you say?"

Twenty francs! So much money. And most of the people in Biel watching him! Adrien stared at the smiling faces around him. He reached out and shook the hand that was offered him. It was happening! he shouted to himself. What he had dreamed about for so long was finally coming true! He, Adrien Wettach, was going to become famous!

All night long the certainty of his fame raced through his mind. And each day, as he waited for the evening of the announced high-wire performance, the excitement of that approaching moment swelled inside him.

Then, finally, came the cool evening at the end of May on which the performance was to take place. From where he stood on the balcony, Adrien could see the gleam of the high wire. It was barely visible as it stretched from the hotel balcony clear across the street to the roof of the three-story cafe.

Bourquin and Adrien had pulled the wire taut. Together they had carefully checked its tightness. The crowds were beginning to gather and mill about excitedly in the street below.

And then, at the very last moment, the impossible happened. Adrien could not believe his ears. Bourquin discovered that there was no way of rigging a safety net below the wire. He threw his hat to the floor and kicked it with his foot. It rolled under the railing and sailed to the street below. "The performance is off!" he shouted. Taking a deep breath, he insisted that without a net the performance would not go on.

Not go on! The performance that Adrien had constructed in his mind every day since he had sat with Bourquin at the small table in his father's cafe! Adrien argued and pleaded with the stern-faced Bourquin with a strength and determination he had never known he possessed. "We *have* to go ahead," he said. "We said we would. The crowds are here, waiting."

"I can't. I won't," Bourquin said firmly. There was no room for argument. It was a simple fact. Without a net, he would not perform. He would not step out onto that wire.

Silent, Adrien stared at the wire's gleam. "All right," he said, *"I'll* go."

"What?" Louis laughed. "You? Adrien," he said, "do not be foolish. You are a *musician*. Yes, and you can walk the rope in your backyard. I've seen you do it many times. And very well, too. But here," Louis gestured toward the thin strand of wire and crowded street below, "this is not your backyard. Look down. See how small the faces are. See how far you have to fall—with only the hard street to catch you!"

"But the people . . ." Adrien protested.

"The people can always go home and come back to-morrow. Tomorrow we'll rig up a net . . . somehow. And then we'll perform."

Adrien would not give in so easily. "My father, ask him."

"Ask him what?" Bourquin demanded.

"To let me walk the rope."

Louis only laughed.

"Please," Adrien insisted. "See what he says."

"All right. He's downstairs. I'll ask." As he started down the stairs, Louis turned to look at Adrien. "But I know what he will say. And so do you."

Adrien did not waste a second. As soon as Louis's head had disappeared down the stairs, the lad grabbed a balancing pole. Lifting one foot over the railing, Adrien carefully placed it atop the narrow strand of wire. The wire grew tighter under his weight. He could feel it sag —and then grow taut. Gripping the balancing pole in both hands, he slowly brought his other foot across the low railing and placed it down in front of the first.

Below, the crowd had suddenly grown silent. Carefully Adrien slid one foot along the wire. Cautiously he stepped away from the safety of the balcony.

Again and again, one foot and then the other moved a short distance along the thin strand of wire.

He could feel the wire's narrowness, its roundness, through his stocking feet.

In his moist hands, the long, heavy balancing pole tipped ever so slightly this way . . . and then, just as slightly, the other.

"I've only to reach . . . the other side," Adrien told himself. He bit his lip. He talked to himself again and again over the sound of the wind.

"I've only to reach the other side," he whispered, "and then . . . then everything will be all right. Everything then will be wonderful," he thought as he edged closer and closer to the end of the wire. At last, he was there. His hands touched the edge of the cafe's roof. When he reached the roof, he realized something he had known in the back of his mind all along.

One trip across the wire really was not enough. Now that he had done this much, he was going to walk back the other way. Only then would both he and his audience be satisfied.

Turning about on the wire, Adrien started back.

Someone stood silhouetted on the balcony. He shouted to Adrien.

But Adrien did not hear him. Instead, he was concentrating on what was happening beneath his feet. Something was wrong!

Hc could feel the wire suddenly sag. The pole slipped from his damp hands and plummeted to the ground. He felt himself falling. Then something hard and thin dug into both his hands. It was the wire.

Adrien held to it. He clung to it for his life. Slowly he pulled himself along, hand over hand. Closer and closer he swung to the balcony and the figure reaching out for him.

Two hands suddenly grabbed him, lifted him over the low railing, and brought him to his feet, while the crowd below roared. Adrien could hear the crowd and feel the two strong arms holding him. He could hear, alongside him, his father's laughter.

Once he had savored the thrill of the crowd and its applause, Adrien knew that he was and had always to be a performer. And once his feet were again firmly planted on solid ground, he also knew that he would not be, ever again, a high-wire performer. Adrien had no desire to make others—or himself—faint. He wanted only to make people laugh.

And he did. Evenings, customers in his father's cafe laughed at Adrien's jokes and his funny skits. Hour after hour Adrien performed for them. And the more they laughed, the more he knew what he wanted to do. Grock the clown had been born.

One day in November, 1896, when snow was falling in the streets of Biel and covering the mountains that surrounded the valley, Adrien gathered up the funny costumes he had made and the greasepaint for his clown face and said good-bye to his family and friends.

Climbing aboard a small wagon, he set off with several other entertainers to seek his fortune in the distant hamlets and towns. It was a strange and, to Adrien, exciting band. There was a trick rider he had met in his father's cafe, a fire-eater with singed eyebrows and red-rimmed eyes, and a beautiful, long-haired, daring tightrope walker.

The winter was cold, and the crowds were sparse and poor. Adrien went from one small traveling group to another. Some had as many as five tents; others, none at all.

Wherever he went, he carried his costumes and makeup in a small basket. Holding a small piece of glass in one hand as a mirror, ducking torrents of rain and snow that leaked through the thin canvas overhead, he made himself up in the flickering light of a candle. Groping about in the damp darkness for his oversized, funny-looking shoes, he slopped in them through the puddles, and leaped, laughing, into the circus ring.

Once inside the ring, Grock set about showing the world that it could not do without him. He would throw open the top of a huge trunk lying in the center of the ring and look inside. Bending low, he would peer into each dark corner. Then, reaching inside, he would pull out a tiny fiddle and hold it up for everyone to see.

Grock would stare, dumbfounded, at the fiddle he held, while the audience laughed to think that such an enormous trunk was needed to hold so tiny an instrument.

The crowd roared again as Grock held the instrument back side up, wondering where the strings had gone. Finally the clown would turn the fiddle over, discover the strings, and play a tune.

Sitting down at a piano, Grock would begin to play another song and then decide that the piano was too far

Photopress • Zurich–Bern–Genf

Near the end of his long career, Grock, in his late sixties, performs on a flower-strewn stage.

away. Getting up from his stool, he would try to push the huge piano closer.

Another clown would enter the ring and begin to pester Grock. Grock would become angry and chase him around the ring, threatening to whack him with the piano lid. Finally tiring of running, Grock would lean the lid against the piano, take off his hat, and set it on top of the lid. He would watch in amusement as the hat slid down the lid to the ground.

Grock would shrug. Then he would climb up on the piano and, sliding down the lid himself, pop the hat back on his head.

Clowns, Grock used to say, were not like actors, who learned their parts word for word from a script and had to stick to a set routine. Clowns were free to make up new things to do every day. Clowns could do anything— anything funny.

Grock was funny, always. His blunders with the fiddle and the piano made people laugh in every country he visited. There was no such thing as a language barrier between Grock and his audiences; the clown was hilarious without speaking a word.

Grock became known throughout the world as the greatest clown of his time. He owned a home so magnificent that a king once asked to buy it. He performed in the most exciting and famous places; and wherever he went, his fans flocked to see him.

Grock enjoyed his fame and success. But what pleased him most of all was that he was doing what he had set out to do—"something spectacular."

One night in the early nineteenth century, a clockmaker's son hurried home through the narrow, lamplit streets of the ancient French town of Bois. Beneath his arm were tucked two books that were about to change his life—miraculously. He was a small lad, slight and shy. But his eyes were bright and glowing. His name was Jean Eugene. But the world came to applaud him as Robert Houdin the Magician.

Robert Houdin

WHEN HE grew up, the boy named Jean Eugene fascinated his audiences with tales of how a traveling conjurer once saved his life and taught him secrets of magic while the two of them toured about the world in the conjurer's horse-drawn wagon.

Which parts of that exciting story actually happened, and which parts were created from the boy's active imagination? No one can really say—for sure. Jean Eugene Robert—or Jean Robert Houdin, as he later became known—believed that a great magician should play the role of a conjurer to the hilt, surrounding himself with mystery and intrigue. He did so, always. At this Robert Houdin was a master.

Long before he ever set foot on a stage or was rescued by any conjurer—real or imagined—Jean Eugene worked as an ordinary clerk in a stuffy, drab, and terribly dull law office. His father was a skilled watchmaker and jeweler. Jean Eugene would gladly have been one, too—if only he were permitted. But his father insisted that the lad become a lawyer.

And so, each day, Jean Eugene sat in his dusty office, copying page after page of legal contracts—none of which he understood or even cared about.

Each day he made neat little marks with his pen and sat waiting for the moment when, at last, his master would clear his throat, straighten his stiff collar, and step out the door on his way to court. Then Jean Eugene would drop his pen, push his papers aside, and concentrate instead on the cage of canaries in the far corner of the old office.

One of Jean Eugene's duties was to feed these birds. His imagination had turned the task into what, to him, was almost a miracle. Over a period of several months, he had built small carts of cardboard, and each day he filled them with food. To reach the food, the canaries learned to tug on a cord and pull the carts into their cage. Jean Eugene had built a special perch, too. When the birds sat on it, they knew they would automatically be rewarded with seed. *This* part of Jean Eugene's job never bored him.

It was always late by the time Jean Eugene was able to put his pens away and leave the office. One day he had worked especially hard, hoping to be able to leave on time, as he had planned to stop at a bookseller's shop on his way home. At sunset he was sure he could not race through the narrow, winding streets and reach the shop before the old man had drawn the shades and locked the door for the evening. But somehow the boy succeeded.

He ran all the way and burst into the shop, asking for the volumes on clockmaking the bookseller had put aside for him. Smiling, the old man took two thick books from a shelf and wrapped them in heavy paper. Paying for them, Jean Eugene hurried off, the bundle under his arm. It was not until he reached his room and tore open the wrapper that he saw the books in his lap were not about clocks at all.

The tired bookseller had made a mistake—but what a glorious mistake! Instead of talking about minute hands and springs and dials, the books in Jean Eugene's hands whispered how he could perform magic tricks with cards and guess another person's thoughts. They even showed him how to cut off the head of a pigeon—and put it back on again!

Jean Eugene lost all sense of time. By morning he had almost finished both books. By the end of the week, he had mastered most of the tricks described in the volumes. He practiced sleight of hand. Wherever he went, his hands were buried deep in his pockets. In the office, on the street, in a restaurant, whether he was working at copying or carrying his books or having dinner—always one hand would be secretly palming coins and corks or lumps of sugar in his pocket.

Jean Eugene practiced juggling, too. He could juggle two, three, and finally even four balls in the air. In time he was able to keep them all in the air *and* read his books at the same time.

Still, each morning Jean Eugene picked up his pen and copied page after dull page in the stuffy law office—that is, until the day when his master returned unexpectedly to find his young clerk building another cardboard toy for the canaries. The lawyer said nothing at the time. But that evening he met with Jean Eugene's father.

Shaking his head, the lawyer said, "Monsieur Robert, I'm sorry. Your son, Jean Eugene, is a fine young man, but *never* will he be a fine young lawyer. His hands are meant to build things—create things—not to copy down lines. And his mind is on creating, not copying. He should be anything . . . anything *but* my apprentice!"

When the lawyer had left, Jean Eugene's father sat down with the young man. To Jean Eugene's delight, his father sighed and said, "You are now *my* apprentice. We begin teaching you in the morning."

Jean Eugene learned quickly. His apprenticeship with his father was soon finished, and the young man went to work for another clockmaker. Shortly after he had established himself in his new job, he married the clockmaker's daughter.

Jean Eugene excelled at his profession. His mind and hands were so sure of their task that often the day's work was finished long before evening. Jean Eugene would spend the rest of the time at the shop building odd mechanical novelties out of the scraps of material around him. One of his creations, a "magical" clock, never failed to amaze anyone who saw it in the shop's window. This strange little clock of glass appeared to have no works inside it at all. There was nothing to see but a clear glass pedestal, a transparent glass clock face, and two slender hands. Nowhere could a gear or a spring or any sort of motor be seen. Yet the perplexing clock not only ran, it kept perfect time.

There were other curiosities, too: mechanical birds that flapped their wings and sang; mechanical dolls that stepped out of colorful boxes and began to dance about; and automatic acrobats that performed tricks on a tightrope. Jean Eugene even created a miniature conjurer, who amused his audience with several tiny cups beneath which were a seemingly endless number of disappearing balls. The young clockmaker created many amazing novelties. But it was Jean Eugene's mysterious clock that one day brought fortune to his door.

A wealthy nobleman, Count de L'Escalopier, came inside the shop one afternoon to ask about it. "That clock," he said. "The curious little glass clock in the window. The one that appears to have no works at all. Did you make it?"

Glancing up from his workbench, Jean Eugene—who, according to the custom of the day, had taken his wife's last name, Houdin, for his own—smiled at his visitor. "Yes," he said as the count closed the door behind him.

"And did you invent it, too?" the visitor asked.

Houdin nodded.

"The idea is yours, then?"

Again, Houdin nodded.

The visitor set his hat down on a corner of the workbench and glanced about him at the small shop filled with Houdin's intriguing creations. Fascinated by all he saw, the count chatted with the young clockmaker. When he left, much later, he took the wonderful glass clock and its secret with him. Setting the clock on the workbench, Houdin had shown the clock's new owner how its works were concealed inside its innocent-looking brass base and connected to the hands by transparent glass rods that moved, unseen, inside its hollow glass pedestal.

The count was delighted with his new treasure. He became a frequent visitor to Houdin's shop. When de L'Escalopier learned that his friend was an amateur magician, he insisted Houdin perform at his home. The count was so impressed by what he saw that he urged

Houdin to perform professionally. He offered to lend the clockmaker money for such a venture, but Houdin's pride kept him from accepting.

Not long afterwards, however, it was the count who came to Houdin in need of help. For some time de L'Escalopier sat staring without saying a word, as Houdin worked on a large, old clock. Houdin knew that something was wrong. At last the count began to tell him the problem.

"For several years now," he began, "I've been the victim of frequent burglaries. Each time my desk has been broken into and my money stolen."

Houdin set down his tools. He listened carefully to what his friend had to say.

"I've tried everything I could think of to stop it," the count continued. He picked up a small gear from the table and turned it over and over in his hand. He set it back down in exactly the same spot from which he had picked it up. "But every attempt I've made has failed. I've no more ideas," he said, looking at Houdin. "But you are filled with ideas. Will you help?"

The next morning, the tired but confident clockmaker showed his friend a mechanism he said would catch the thief. "When the lock in your desk is turned," he explained as he began demonstrating the device, "and the desk lid is raised—like so—this pistol will fire a blank cartridge. The blank is harmless, of course," he added, "but the explosion will warn you of what is happening. At the same instant," Houdin continued, pointing to another part of the strange device, "*this* steel rod will spring down and scratch the thief's hand. With the shot to bring you running and the scratch to point him out to you, this mechanism will catch your thief."

Several days went by without incident. Then, in the middle of the morning, a single shot echoed through the count's home. Rushing toward the sound, de L'Escalopier met his business agent in the study. The agent pointed frantically toward another hallway. Together, the two men raced down the hallway until they came to a stop against a locked door. The count stared down at the lock. The key was still resting in the key hole. The count reasoned that the thief could not possibly have slipped past the door and then locked it from the count's side. And he and the agent had not passed anyone in the narrow hallway. In his confusion, the count turned to his friend.

Something unexpected caught his eye. Reaching out, the count seized the right hand that the agent held stiffly behind his back. The agent cried out in pain as the count's fingers gripped a fresh scratch across the back of his hand. The agent confessed that it was he who had robbed the count so many times before. That day he returned the 15,000 francs that remained of all that he had stolen. L'Escalopier maintained that Houdin had saved him many times that sum by unmasking the thief. He insisted that Houdin take the money and open a theater where he could perform his magic.

Houdin found a small hall over the archway leading to the garden of the Palais Royale. It was an ideal location for a theater, a pleasant building on one of Paris's busiest and most fashionable boulevards. The landlord had said it would seat no more than two hundred. But this was exactly the size Houdin wanted. He was determined to make his magic unique, to make it come alive before his audiences. He disliked the phony hocus-pocus of most magicians, who huffed and puffed about, clumsily concealing their tricks beneath flowing robes and under draped tables that—barely—covered their assistants. Instead, Houdin designed a hall that resembled a comfortable living room. His tables were made of transparent glass and kept uncovered. And he dressed in ordinary clothes, as if he were one of the guests himself. The theater was named simply The Robert Houdin. His act was called "The Enchanted Evening."

The first performance began at eight o'clock on what, for Houdin, was the exciting and nerve-racking evening of July 3, 1845. For him, it was a terrible night. In fact, it was almost his last performance. Long before the curtain rose, he was tense and frightened. By the time the show was over he was sure his worst fears had been confirmed. The audience, he told himself over and over again, only applauded out of kindness. He swore that he would never perform in public again.

The next night, when a small crowd gathered outside the theater, they found that The Robert Houdin was closed. It might never have opened again. But then an acquaintance of Houdin complimented him on his good sense in giving up the stage. Houdin was hurt—and furious. Immediately he began rehearsing the next evening's show. Night after night he performed, with never another word of quitting. Always, the theater was crowded. The critics came and left to write glowing reviews. Soon the "Enchanted Evenings" of Robert Houdin were the talk of all Paris.

Each evening began as the host walked down the aisle. He smiled at his guests and apologized for not having arrived earlier. "But I promise," he added, "to begin instantly." Drawing a pistol from beneath his jacket, he fired a shot toward the darkened stage. Suddenly, the stage glowed in the light of a hundred flickering candles. Houdin stepped upon the magnificently illuminated stage and bowed. He showed his audience a clock face. It reminded some of them of his famous clock, except this one had only one hand. Spinning it, Houdin asked his audience to pick a number. "Any number," he invited. "Whatever comes to your mind."

Someone called out, say, the number five. And the hand stopped, mysteriously frozen at that number.

Taking a deck of cards from his coat pocket, Houdin asked his audience to choose one. "Ten of clubs," someone said. And the card rose out of the deck. Houdin bowed, and then produced—out of nowhere, it seemed—a large bowl filled with water and splashing goldfish.

Pausing, he wiped his forehead with a handkerchief. He was about to put it in his pocket, but it disappeared! Smiling and shrugging his shoulders as though such things always happened to magicians, Houdin pointed toward a small orange tree.

The audience looked, and as they did, the tree blossomed. They applauded, and the tree bore fruit.

Golden coins vanished from Houdin's hands, suddenly reappearing as they tumbled into a crystal casket that hung suspended over the stage. Houdin opened a suitcase that was no bigger than a desk drawer and from it produced hats, bird cages, and finally, his son Emile. The magician tipped an enchanted bottle and poured seemingly endless streams of whatever drink his guests suggested.

Setting his props aside, Houdin told his audience

Houdin instructs his son Eugene in some of the secrets of his profession.

that he had been experimenting lately with a new discovery—ether. He told how he had found it "even more
potent than medical science supposes." While he dis-
cussed the scientific theory that ether could deaden the
feeling of pain, his youngest son, Eugene, stepped across
the stage and stood upon a high stool. Houdin continued
talking about the "miracle substance" while he spread the
boy's arms and placed them so that his elbows rested
atop two upright poles set into the stage floor.

Still talking about the powers of ether, Houdin took a
small bottle from his coat pocket, unscrewed its cap, and
appeared to let Eugene inhale its contents. The audience
leaned forward in their seats when they, too, smelled the
pungent odor. They stared as the boy's eyes began to
shut. While they stared, his head dropped forward.

Gently, Houdin lifted his son's head and rested it on
one of the boy's upraised hands. Reaching down, Houdin
glanced quickly at his audience—and then carefully
pulled the stool out from under the boy's feet. There was
a gasp as the bewildered audience stared at the sight of
the small boy rigidly suspended, or so it seemed, on his
elbows between the two thin poles!

Then, before anyone in the audience could close his
mouth, Houdin had grabbed one of the poles and
snatched it from beneath the boy's elbow. The audience
were almost on their feet. But the boy was still asleep—
supported, miraculously, it seemed, by only one pole.

Gently, as if afraid of upsetting the delicate balance
he had created, Houdin swung the boy's free arm down to
his side. Grasping both his son's feet, Houdin slowly
swung the small boy upward, so that when the conjurer
let go, the boy seemed suspended in mid-air.

No one took his eyes away from the strange sight. No one could say, for certain, how long the boy hung there. Some said for only a minute. Others said more like ten. Then, as though he sensed his son were about to awaken, Houdin quickly lowered him back to his original position, raised his free arm, and propping the pole beneath it, returned the stool beneath the boy's feet. As if on signal, Eugene's eyes fluttered open. Without a word, he returned the audience's curious gaze.

Many years later Houdin wrote in a book—the same book that a boy named Ehrich Weiss would one day happen to read—that "sleight of hand must not be the tinman's work, but the artist's." Houdin's "ethereal suspension," like most of his tricks, was a perfect example of his conviction. His son's jacket concealed a metal framework that was strapped to his back. A metal support slipped into a socket on one of the poles, and a ratchet made it possible for the boy to be swung up and down. With this device the boy could "float" when the stool and the other pole were taken away. Knowing the secret of the trick, anyone could do it. The mechanism was the "tinman's work."

But it was Houdin's art, his suggestion that the mysterious new substance, ether, was responsible for the feat, and his dramatic mixture of fatherly concern and supreme self-confidence, that made the illusion so unforgettable. For days, his audience talked of how they still smelled ether. Ether? There had been none, of course, in the bottle. But the audience had smelled it. The odor had come from the few drops of ether that Houdin's other son, Emile, dropped on a hot skillet backstage at the exact moment that Houdin uncapped the empty bottle.

One of Houdin's most famous feats was performed before King Louis-Philippe of France. A salon in the royal palace was prepared especially for Houdin. Outside it was a warm June day, and the palace windows were opened wide on an elegantly manicured garden lined with orange trees. Houdin did several of his most famous tricks. Then he borrowed six handerchiefs from the courtiers, asking the owner of each to mark his or hers so as to be sure to recognize it later. The magician passed around sheets of paper and explained that he was going to make the handkerchiefs disappear. But first he wanted each person to suggest a place to send the handkerchiefs.

Gathering the answers, Houdin fanned them in his hand like a deck of cards. He asked the king to choose three answers, read them, and then select the one that he preferred.

The king did so, reading all three out loud. "Under the candelabra on the mantel" he thought too simple a stunt for such a wonderful magician to do. "To the dome of a famous building" he considered a challenge—but one too difficult to check. The third, "Beneath the third orange tree on the right of the corridor," was more to his liking. Nodding his agreement, the king ordered his attendants to guard the tree. Then he motioned to Houdin to continue.

Bowing, Houdin placed the handkerchiefs under a bowl. He tapped the bowl once. Then saying, "The handkerchiefs are gone," he lifted the cover a few inches. Something white—a turtledove—fluttered out. It perched on a nearby chandelier. Houdin raised the bowl still further. Indeed, the handkerchiefs were gone.

At a signal from the king, an attendant dug beneath

the tree in the garden. His spade cut through the earth several times and then struck something metal. His fingers found a small, rusted iron box and rescued it from the tangle of roots that held it. The dirt and mold were cleaned off, and then the box was handed to the king. It was locked. Without a word, Houdin lifted the turtledove down from its perch and showed the king the key that hung around its neck.

The king opened the box and smiled. Inside were six handkerchiefs—the same six handkerchiefs, according to their owners, that had earlier been given to Houdin. The box also contained a piece of yellowed parchment. "Today, the sixth of June, 1786," the king read, "this iron box, containing six handkerchiefs, was placed among the roots of an orange tree by myself, Balsama, Count of Cagliostro, to serve in performing an act of magic, which will be executed on the same day sixty years hence before Louis-Philippe of Orleans and his family."

Cagliostro! There was not a soul in the royal palace or in all of France who had not heard of this famous conjurer. He had lived years before and had used the secrets of magic not to entertain but to deceive. One by one, the members of the court turned their awed and curious faces toward their neighbors. Was it possible? Could it really be? One of the courtiers pointed in silence toward the seal embedded in the wax at the bottom of the page. He was sure the signature and the seal were Cagliostro's. Later an expert proved him right.

Houdin was able to "send" the handkerchiefs to the right spot because he knew beforehand that that was the place the king would choose. At the right moment, Houdin switched his audience's suggestions for others he had already written. He listed only three places, and he fanned the choices in his hand in such a way that the king was led to pick one of each. Houdin believed that the king would choose the orange tree for the very reason the king gave—it was both difficult for the conjurer and easy for the king. [Other handkerchiefs inside similar boxes had been concealed in the two alternate hiding places, in case the king surprised Houdin. Houdin would have switched those handerchiefs for the borrowed ones when *he* opened the box.]

But the king did choose as Houdin had anticipated. When the magician covered the borrowed handerchiefs with the bowl, they slipped into a secret compartment in the table as planned—the same compartment that, until then, had held the turtledove. While Houdin passed out the slips of paper, his son removed the handerchiefs from their hiding place and carried them into the garden, where he put them inside the iron box and buried it in the loose soil before the guards arrived. The signature on the letter? Houdin copied it from one of Cagliostro's letters. The seal? Houdin had bought it many years before from an antique dealer and saved it especially for just such an occasion.

After performing for the king, Houdin retired. But even in retirement his magic was in demand. One day a government official, looking very stiff and uncomfortable in his uniform, asked Houdin to come out of retirement for one more spectacular show.

"I have been asked by our government to make a request," the visitor explained, after complimenting Houdin on his worldwide reputation. "I've been asked to request you to perform once more."

Houdin studied his visitor questioningly.

"Not to entertain," the official said, as though he had

anticipated Houdin's thoughts and was answering them, "but to mystify."

The official went on to say that the French government needed Houdin to help quell a native revolt in Algiers. He explained that Arab wizards, called *marabouts,* were stirring up the tribal leaders with claims that they could perform miracles that no Frenchman could overcome. Spurred on by the wizards, Arab bands were attacking French outposts. Even Algiers itself, the official stressed, was threatened. "Only one person can end this uprising without bloodshed," the official continued, leaning forward in his chair. "Our government hopes that your magic will bring an end to the terror.

"I must warn you," the official went on, his eyes on the carpet between them, "a favorite trick of the *marabouts* is to have a pistol fired at them point-blank."

Then the official stared at his host. "The bullet is aimed at their hearts. But never, *never,*" he repeated, "is there even a scratch. Probably you will have to duplicate the trick."

Houdin looked at his visitor and smiled.

Algiers was hot and sticky, and Houdin wiped the sweat from his forehead. More than sixty grim-faced Arab chieftains stared at him from their places of honor at the front of the theater. Houdin stepped to the middle of the small Algerian stage and bowed. Only silence greeted him. He listened to the interpreter repeating his greeting in the chieftains' own languages. Still there was only silence as, smiling, he began his performance. Never before had he felt such excitement—and anxiety.

The chieftains stared at the strange little Frenchman, who again and again produced cannonballs from his hat.

They watched as, out of nowhere, Houdin produced bouquets of sweet-smelling flowers. They looked on as he scooped dozens of heaping plates of sweetmeats from a small and seemingly empty silver bowl, and then stared in disbelief as he poured strong, steaming coffee from the bowl, so that all of them could eat and drink.

Leaning forward on their cushions, the Arabs listened as the amazing stranger carried a small wooden box to the front of the stage. "I can deprive the most powerful man of his strength," Houdin stated quietly, "and restore it at my will."

The Frenchman paused, waiting for the interpreters to finish. He stared at the intent faces around him. "Who will come forward," he asked, "to show his strength?"

A gigantic man with huge, powerful arms climbed the steps to the stage. He laughed as he took the small box and juggled it in one enormous hand. Then he set it down, and Houdin swept his hands over the chieftain.

"I'm taking the strength from your body," Houdin shouted. "Draining your strength away!"

The chieftain only smiled at this strange man—until he heard the interpreter. Then he bent down and seized the box by its handles. He yanked at it. It did not move.

"Your fellow chieftain is weaker than a child," Houdin told his audience. Panting and red with fury, the Arab pulled and tugged again. Suddenly he fell to his knees, screaming. Quickly Houdin passed his hands over the figure on the floor. The man leaped to his feet and ran from the theater, crying out in fear.

Houdin asked his wide-eyed audience if anyone would like to shoot him. If so, Houdin said, he would show that he had the power to prevent bullets from hurting him, just as the *marabouts* had.

A figure in a long, flowing robe leaped to the stage, swearing to kill the conjurer. Houdin handed him a pistol, powder, and a lead ball, and asked the chieftain to mark the ball with his dagger. Holding an apple stuck on a knife in front of him, Houdin told the Arab to aim for his heart. The Arab pulled the trigger, and a shot rang out. But instead of collapsing on the floor, Houdin broke open the apple and held up the marked bullet for everyone to see.

Another chieftain jumped to the stage, swearing he would shoot the French devil with his *own* pistol. Houdin handed him a bullet to mark. The chieftain loaded his pistol with it and fired.

Houdin stumbled, and just as the chieftains rose to their feet shouting, he stood up and spat the marked bullet from between his teeth.

Taking the pistol from the astounded chieftain's hands, he reloaded it with another ball and fired it at the theater wall. A red blob splashed against the wall and ran down its side. Houdin spun around to his audience. "Any of you who would challenge my magic," he shouted, pointing toward the spotted wall and the startled Arabs, "remember, this man's soul is mine now. I've drawn the blood from his shadow!"

The frightened chieftain ran from the theater. Houdin asked for another volunteer, but no one came forward. He asked again, and finally another Arab stepped onto the stage. Nervously he followed Houdin's request that he stand upon a table. A large cone was slowly lowered over the Arab. Several restless moments went by. Then the cone was lifted. There was no one there!

The audience disappeared almost as quickly. Terrified, the chieftains fled the awesome Frenchman, whose magic seemed so much more powerful than that of their own wizards.

Before returning to France and his home, Houdin instructed his country's officials to explain to the chieftains that his magical deeds were simply tricks. He told them how the Arab chieftain who had vanished beneath the cone was really an accomplice disguised as an Arab. Under cover of the cone, the assistant had slipped through the table's hidden panel and disappeared beneath it.

The strong man who had lost his strength? Houdin explained that the wooden box had a metal lining. Beneath the stage, he said, a huge electric magnet, which he could turn off and on at will, made it impossible for anyone to lift the box when Houdin did not want him to.

And the *marabouts'* trick—the bullets that could hurt neither them nor Houdin? He had substituted wax bullets for the real ones. They were dyed to look like lead bullets and disintegrated when the gun was fired. Houdin squeezed the first lead bullet into a notch he had already made in the apple. He hid the second lead bullet in his mouth. For the next trick, Houdin loaded the pistol with a wax bullet filled with red dye. The disappearing chieftain, the weakling-strongman, the magician who, like the wizards, could not be shot—they were all just tricks, Houdin explained, which he made seem real.

Jean Eugene returned to France and home. But he never forgot his magical evenings, nor did all the crowds who wondered at them.

As a boy, Phineas Taylor Barnum was a fast-talking, lanky Connecticut Yankee with thick, curly hair, a prominent nose, and an odd-sounding, high-pitched voice. Like his grandfather and father, his uncles, and in fact, everyone he had ever known, Barnum loved a practical joke. He grew up to become the most outlandish jokester of them all. With glee he hoaxed, bamboozled, tricked, shocked, and entertained crowds all over the world. And they laughed, loved him for it, and swore that Barnum, the "Old Humbug," was the greatest spectacle of them all.

Phineas T. Barnum

G<small>EORGE</small>'s Nurse Tells All!"

One day in 1835 New Yorkers picked up their newspapers and read about Joice Heth, an old Negro woman
who claimed to have been George Washington's nurse.
Aunt Joice, the papers said, was cheerful and healthy and
full of anecdotes about her young charge. At first glance,
the story did not seem very newsworthy. But Washington
had already been dead for many years, and Aunt Joice,
according to the newspapers, was 161 years old!

One paper, the *New York Evening Star*, said Aunt
Joice looked "like an Egyptian mummy just escaped from
its sarcophagus."

Folks read the strange tale that evening and again the
next morning on their way to work. They argued about
it at lunch, and then many of them hurried to the place
where the papers said Aunt Joice could be seen—for a
small fee. Those who visited Aunt Joice were startled to
see that, for once, the papers had not exaggerated.

Joice Heth lay on a shabby couch, her skeleton-like
legs drawn up against her body. A hundred and sixty-one

years old? She might have been a thousand! Her eyeballs were sunk so deeply in their sockets that they almost seemed to have disappeared. She was toothless, and her wrinkled face was topped by a dense bush of gray-white hair. Her left arm lay across her thin chest. The nails on the tips of her fragile fingers were longer than her thumb. Her right arm was the only part of her that moved. As she talked, the five fingers of her right hand flickered back and forth in the air.

Old Joice talked mostly about "little George." She had been a house slave, she said, and was present when little George was born. "It was me who clothed him," she said. "In fact," she boasted, her fingers sending five skinny shadows scurrying across the wall, "it was me that raised him."

On and on she talked in her thin, dusty voice. When she didn't talk, she sang—old spirituals that few remembered ever hearing before. Those who did hadn't heard the songs since they were children themselves.

More and more people crowded into the small room to see Aunt Joice, to ask her questions about the Washingtons, and to hear her stories about "little George." And in a corner of the room, the sly, smiling man who had written the newspaper letters that said "Joice Heth is unquestionably the most astonishing and interesting curiosity in the world," sat quietly counting the crowd.

P. T. Barnum had been born twenty-five years before on July 5, moments after the fireworks and shouting for the Glorious Fourth had ended. He had not missed another chance to celebrate since. And sitting there smiling and counting the crowd, he had plenty of cause to celebrate. He and Joice, he told himself, were going to be a success.

Barnum was right. Within a week all New York was talking about Aunt Joice. Everyone who had not already crowded into her room seemed to be outside waiting in line. For weeks, crowds came and stared and went. Barnum sat back and counted his profits. And when the crowds finally began to dwindle, he picked up his pen and wrote another letter to the newspapers.

"Joice Heth," New Yorkers read the next day, "is a humbug, the most curious and interesting humbug that anyone has ever seen.

"Joice Heth is not a human being at all," Barnum wrote, "but is made of whalebone, India rubber, and numberless strings ingeniously put together and made to move at the slightest touch. The exhibitor," everyone read, "is a ventriloquist, and all the conversations apparently held with the old lady are purely imaginary." Barnum signed the letter, "A Visitor."

The next day the crowds were bigger and more curious than ever. Those who had never seen Joice rushed to see what had fooled everyone else. And those who had been there before hurried back to see if they really had been mistaken.

Phineas T. Barnum was clearly an imaginative and enterprising young man. But when he was a boy, his neighbors in the small, quiet town of Bethel, Connecticut, used to nod their gray heads and tell each other that the oldest Barnum boy was the laziest lad in the state.

He was really not lazy. Actually, Phineas was quick to do anything he wanted to do. But at the same time, he would go to all sorts of trouble to dig himself out of doing something he did not like.

Folks called the boy lazy because he especially disliked

what most people thought of as work. Phineas was too eager to make money to be lazy. But he wanted to work with his head—not his hands or his back.

When Phineas was twelve, his father put him to work as a clerk in his store. There, his father thought, Phineas would have an opportunity to sharpen his wits. In Barnum's time, New England shopkeepers and their customers had a running battle to see who could get the best of the other. A shopkeeper who was not alert was likely to find that a bundle of rags he had taken in trade was weighted down inside with stones, or that a fifty-bushel load of oats he had purchased was actually five bushels short.

Phineas did well in his new job. He kept a sharp but friendly eye on his customers and drove a hard bargain. And he even started a side business of his own; a penny-candy counter.

Then when Phineas was fifteen, his father died, and the family was left bankrupt. They lost their store, and the young Barnum went to work clerking in another. The boy's new employer was sure that Phineas was bright. Soon enough, he had proof of the fact.

One day when Barnum was alone in the shop, a peddler with a wagonload of old green bottles stopped by the store. Seeing the young boy behind the counter, he decided to try his luck at unloading some of the old bottles. He was astonished to hear Barnum offer to trade for the whole lot.

Barnum's boss could not believe his eyes when he returned to the shop that afternoon. Everywhere he looked there were piles of useless green bottles.

The boy quickly explained about the peddler and his

bottles and how he had managed to pay him off with some of the store's clutter of unsalable junk.

Barnum's boss wasted no time in telling Phineas that he had made a fool of himself. But the boy replied that he would be rid of every bottle in three months. He did not tell his employer about how he planned to accomplish that feat. But he already had a scheme in mind.

A few days later Barnum hung a poster outside the store. *Magnificent lottery,* it announced in bright, bold letters. *$25 for only 50 cents!!! Over 550 prizes!!! Only 1,000 tickets!!!*

The tickets sold almost as quickly as folks could read the sign. But it was not until the day of the drawing, when the prizes were handed out, that anyone realized that all of the prizes were old green bottles and rusty tinware that had been lying around the store for years. The townspeople were angry at first. But finally they had to laugh at themselves for being taken in by such a joke. They all agreed that young P. T. Barnum was a lot smarter than he was lazy.

It was one of the prize winners who, years later, first told Barnum about the amazing woman named Joice Heth.

After Barnum published his second letter to the newspapers, claiming that the woman advertised as George Washington's nurse was nothing more than a ventriloquist's dummy, his exhibit flourished. Joice Heth and Barnum continued to draw in the crowds for months.

Then, suddenly, Joice Heth died. The famous surgeon who performed the autopsy said that "instead of being 161 years old, Joice was probably not over 80." Hearing the news, Barnum swore that he had been tricked by the man who had brought Joice to him. Then he left New York and joined a traveling circus as ticket taker and ringmaster. He left the circus to team up with a juggler. Business—and, in truth, the juggler—were bad, and the two of them had to leave their wagon in one town and their horse in the next to pay their bills. Things went from bad to worse. In one village an angry customer threatened Barnum with a pistol. And in the next an angrier crowd nearly tarred and feathered him. Barnum was only too glad to get back to New York—especially when he heard the American Museum was for sale.

Barnum had visited the museum often and had shuddered at its motheaten collection of stuffed animals, dusty wax figures, old torn banners, flags, and queer objects brought back by roving sea captains. Each time Barnum had poked about in the museum's dingy corners, he had thought of all that he could do to make the dismal old place lively and exciting—if only it were *his*.

New York in Barnum's day had no zoos or amusement parks. There was really nowhere for people to go for exotic sights and unusual entertainment. Barnum was convinced that, given the chance, he could turn the old stone building into a spectacular amusement place. All Barnum, who hadn't an extra penny to his name, had to do—somehow—was buy it.

Some people, having no money, might have shrugged their shoulders, mumbled "too bad," and gone on their way. But not Barnum. He picked up a pen and wrote to the owner of the five-story building in which the museum was housed. He told the landlord he wanted to buy the museum but, since he had no money, he wanted the landlord to give him a loan. Barnum assured the landlord that since he was such a fine showman, he would undoubtedly be able to repay the loan with unprecedented speed.

Something in the boldness of Barnum's letter caught the landlord's eye, and he agreed to lend Barnum the money. In January, 1842, Phineas T. Barnum became the proprietor of the American Museum.

Each morning at dawn, Barnum flung open his museum's doors. He never closed them until late at night. He found and brought trained flea circuses, dwarfs, giants, knife throwers, and magicians into the museum. He searched for the worst-sounding, noisiest band he could find and put it outside on the balcony overlooking the front doors. Then he told the bandsmen to play as loud as they could. The racket, he said once he was back inside, might send even more customers scurrying in, just to get away from the noise.

One night Barnum asked his workmen to hang huge, colorful portraits of all the strange creatures he could imagine between the windows on all five floors. In the morning, stunned crowds stared in amazement at the fanciful sight of leopards, snakes, and zebras swarming over the museum's walls. When night came, Barnum set brilliant gaslights blazing so his museum and creatures could be seen around the clock.

One morning a man walked into the museum and asked the showman for a job. Barnum handed him five bricks. "Set one on the corner," he said, pointing toward the end of the block. "Walk to the next corner and put one there, and another on the next, and so on until you've circled the whole block. Then take the fifth brick and

Phineas Taylor Barnum

exchange it for the first. Keep going around the block carrying a brick with you and changing it at each corner for the one already there.

"Remember," Barnum told his new employee, "don't talk to anyone. If somebody asks what you're doing, pretend you can't hear. Don't listen. Don't stop. Never smile. And when the clock on the church across the way strikes the hour, show this ticket at the door and come inside. Walk through every hall once, and then go back outside. Keep circling the block," Barnum said, "exchanging the bricks as you go, until the next hour strikes."

A curious crowd began to eye the man as soon as he set the first brick down. Around and around the block the man went, followed by the crowd. Each time they passed the museum's front doors, the crowd was bigger and more curious. When the clock struck the hour, the employee showed his ticket and stepped inside. The crowd rushed to buy tickets and follow him. For days, crowds followed the man around the block and into the museum. Barnum would have kept his employee circling the block forever—if the police had not finally insisted that the congestion was unsafe and had to stop.

Barnum loved crowds and commotions. Once he decided a poster announcing a famous violinist was not drawing enough people. He took a look at the poster and ordered it rehung—upside down. People saw the poster and swarmed inside, anxious to see the odd fellow who played the violin while standing on his head.

Before long so many people were pouring into his museum that Barnum had to think of new places to put them, so that those waiting in line outside could get in, too. Gathering together a few chairs and a dozen pots of wilted flowers, he carried them up to the roof. Then he had a sign painted saying *Aerial Garden* and nailed it above the stairs. He had another lettered *To The Egress*. Visitors saw the odd sign and followed its arrow, wondering what sort of rare creature was the "egress" they were about to see. They hurried along down a narrow flight of stairs and out through a narrow doorway. There they stood, blinking in the bright daylight, with no chance of getting back into the museum without waiting once more in line to pay the price of another admission at the ticket window.

One day the son of a sea captain brought something for Barnum to see. While in Japan, years before, the visitor explained, his father had spent most of his ship's money to buy a mermaid. The ship's owners didn't believe that anything that looked so ugly was worth their money, and the old captain had spent the rest of his life working to pay back the money.

Barnum stared at the curiosity in his hands. It looked like a monkey's head atop a fish's body. Its shoulders were covered with thick hair. From head to tail, the odd creature was about three feet long. It was dried up and dark and had a hideous, ugly face half hidden behind hands thrown up to cover its wide-open mouth. Its teeth were small and sharp. They gleamed in a mouth that looked as though it were about to shout.

"It can't be real," a professor told Barnum. "I've never seen a monkey with such teeth or arms or hands—or a fish that had such fins. Yet," he admitted, "I can't imagine how it was made."

Barnum stared at the professor. "Then why are you so sure it was?" he asked.

Over his glasses, the professor returned Barnum's stare. "Because I don't believe in mermaids," he replied.

Barnum laughed, quite happy with the answer. "Then my reason for thinking it's real," he said, "is as good as yours for thinking it isn't. From now on I'm going to believe in them."

Barnum knew he would not have to convince people to believe in mermaids to make his new curiosity a success. All he had to do was to talk them into believing that mermaids *might* exist. If he could do that, then everyone would rush to gaze at the strange creature and judge for himself whether or not it was real.

Barnum busied himself writing more letters to the newspapers. Soon everybody was reading about the strange creature and gazing up in wonder at the gigantic banner that hung above the museum's doors and pictured a beautiful mermaid.

Another of Barnum's biggest sensations was less than two feet tall. Before Barnum rechristened him, his name was Charles Stratton, and he was five years old. He was bright and healthy, but for no apparent reason, he suddenly had stopped growing when he was seven months old. He was strong and good-looking, with dark, shining eyes under a shock of blonde hair, but he weighed only fifteen pounds. His feet were only three inches long, and his hands were no larger than a half dollar.

Barnum took one look at the boy and renamed him Tom Thumb—General Tom Thumb. He took a second look and decided that five years old sounded very young. People might figure that Tom still had a long time to grow. And so Barnum made up his mind that General Thumb was not really five, but eleven. The "Old Humbug" also thought that Tom's hometown in Connecticut did not sound like a very exciting place from which to come. Everyone, Barnum told himself, knew people from Connecticut. And so, according to Barnum, eleven-year-old General Tom Thumb had just arrived in the United States from England.

Tom was so popular that Barnum decided that a tour of Europe was in order. Barnum, the "General," and Tom's parents sailed for London, where Barnum rented a mansion in an exclusive section of the city. Only the best of the neighboring millionaires and lords received invitations to come and visit Tom Thumb.

Soon General Tom was the most talked about person in London. Barnum rented the Egyptian Hall, where a popular magician named Houdin had been playing, and the crowds poured in. Barnum was impressed with what he heard about Houdin. He bought one of the magician's creations—a life-sized figure seated at a desk, which could draw pictures of a dog and jot down the magician's signature or even the time of day on a sheet of paper— and sent it back to the museum.

One night people came to the theater only to find a notice posted outside. *Closed for the Evening,* it said, *General Tom Thumb Being at Buckingham Palace by Command of Her Majesty.*

Again and again, Tom Thumb visited the kings and queens of Europe. In France Barnum and Tom Thumb were guests of the king. In Spain they entertained Queen Isabella. And in Brussels they were guests of King Leopold. Several years passed in this way before they finally returned to the United States. By that time both Barnum and General Tom were famous throughout the world.

Returning to Connecticut, Barnum built his own oriental castle and topped it with glittering spires and shining, onion-shaped domes that glowed a hundred feet or more in the sky. Elk and reindeer played near bubbling fountains that dotted the estate's rich green lawns. Always eager for more publicity, Barnum built his castle alongside the railroad tracks to New York City. A keeper, dressed in an Indian turban, silk breeches, and a yellow tunic, hitched a plow to an elephant whenever a train was scheduled to pass. The passengers stared in wonder at the majestic creature and its master plowing Mr. Barnum's cornfield alongside the track.

Historical Pictures Service • Chicago

Barnum's mansion near Bridgeport, Connecticut

In the spring of 1871, Barnum presented what he called the "World's First Mammoth Circus." He also called it a "Museum, Menageria, Caravan, Hippodrome, and Circus Spectacular All in One!" It *was* big. Enormous tents covered acres of showgrounds; Barnum's circus boasted the largest stretch of canvas ever spread. More than five hundred men and battalions of elephants and horses were needed to set up the vast tent. When they were through, more than ten thousand awed spectators could crowd together in its coolness.

Colorful posters announcing the wonders and thrills of the circus suddenly appeared on barns and fences for seventy-five miles around the showgrounds. The "Greatest Show on Earth" boasted a waxworks, the Eldorado Elf, a Palestinian giant in whose hands the tiny elf often sat, Fiji Island cannibals, a bearded boy, an Italian goat who rode horseback, and a mechanical Sleeping Beauty who was said to breathe and gasp. Hamlets, crossroads, villages, towns, and cities—the whole country—found its way inside Barnum's huge tents. His show became so popular, so extraordinary, that when it came to a town, everything else stopped. Signs appeared on factory doors: *Closed on Account of the Greatest Interference on Earth.*

Every morning as the circus rolled into a new sleeping town, a cannon was fired to remind anyone foolish enough to have forgotten that the day was Circus Day. Each night the great spectacle ended with cascades of fireworks. Between the cannon and the skyrockets came all the delights of the "Greatest Show on Earth."

The secret of its wonder, Barnum was convinced, was the circus's overwhelming size. It was huge, sprawling, and enormous. Barnum's show seemed to fill the whole town and all the countryside around it. After the first successful season, Barnum decided to make his show even bigger and more spectacular.

The next year it emerged from winter quarters more than twice as big as it had been before. It was "so huge," people said, "it couldn't possibly be moved by elephants and horses and men alone." But Barnum had figured out how to transport everything—tents and seats and animals and performers and props—by train. Seventy long railroad cars carried the canvases and animals and props. Six more carried the circus people. It took three engines to pull them all along. Night after night the colorful circus trains carried the "Greatest Show on Earth" over gleaming railroad tracks from one sleeping city to the next.

In each city, Barnum noticed how much the public liked the idea of having so much to look at that they could not possibly watch it all at once. Always one to give folks what they liked, Barnum had another ring installed in the main tent, and he put on two shows at the same time. The crowds loved the second ring so much that Barnum added a third. To this day, every circus worth its boasts brags about having three rings.

For years, no other circus could compare with Barnum's. Then in 1880 another traveling show boldly appeared in what until then had always been "Barnum's towns." When Barnum heard that one of the brash new show's elephants had had a baby, the first elephant born in America, Barnum wired the rival show and offered to pay a hundred thousand dollars for the mother and child.

One of the show's owners, James A. Bailey, astonished Barnum by wiring back that he could keep his money— and they would keep their elephants! Barnum was even more flabbergasted when, several days later, he saw huge posters plastered around the countryside with a picture of his telegram and, in enormous letters, the words: *What Barnum Thinks of Our Baby Elephant.*

Then Barnum knew that, at last, he had met the man who could give him a run for his money. At seventy,

Barnum was growing a bit fat and—almost—ready to slow down. Barnum arranged a meeting with the young, wiry Bailey, and together they made a deal. The next spring, in a torchlight parade cheered on by half of Manhattan, the Barnum and Bailey "Greatest Show on Earth" paraded down Broadway for the first time. A calliope played, bells chimed, a steam organ joined in, and a squad of Scottish bagpipers blew while a choir of black Jubilee singers sang and four brass bands tooted and drummed and clanged.

In front and behind and on both sides came hundreds of circus animals, brightly colored circus wagons, countless clowns, daring men, and beautiful circus women.

At last, true to his boasts and ballyhoo, Barnum was the producer of the "Greatest Show on Earth." Wherever the circus traveled, the whole countryside thronged to see it. And the man who ran it, Barnum, was the greatest spectacle of all.

"Clowns," Barnum once said, "are pegs used to hang circuses on." Chances are that the "Old Humbug" was thinking of Dan Rice. Dan was the most popular, hilarious clown ever to bring a circus by riverboat up the Mississippi—and wherever else rivers, spunk, and his restless love of sidesplitting, uproarious adventure could take him.

Dan Rice

A BSOLUTELY right, Lord Byron," the voice on the other side of the low fence said. "It *is* a swell day for wallowing in the mud."

The two young eavesdroppers frowned. They stared at each other. Then they leaned forward and listened again. They *must* have heard wrong, they thought. But no—the voice repeated the very same words again.

"Yes, sir," it said. "It *is* a swell day for wallowing in the mud. Yes, siree, Lord Byron, you're positively right."

The two eavesdroppers pressed both hands against their mouths and smothered the sound of their laughter. Still, they laughed so hard they were sure they would be heard. Apparently they were not. The voice on the other side of the fence kept right on talking.

"If you don't mind my saying so, Lord Byron," the voice continued, "there is *one* thing that's bothering me. That's the way you carried on in that last town. The folks back there were such *nice* people. And they liked you so much. . . ."

There was a long silence, and the two eavesdroppers pressed their ears tightly against the fence. Finally they heard a low, snorting sound.

"Say what you want, Lord Byron," the first voice replied. "They *did* like you. Why, they went about saying what a distinguished sort Lord Byron was. And how educated you were. And how smart. I heard them, many times, saying exactly that."

This time the snorting sound was louder and mixed with high-pitched laughter. It sounded almost like a squeal.

"Well, I only hope you behave better here in this town, Lord Byron. I really hope you do."

The two eavesdroppers stared at each other again. Without a word, they slowly raised their heads and cautiously peered over the top of the fence. There on the other side, sitting with his back to them, was the stranger they had seen walking into town earlier that morning. Across from him, Lord Byron—or the creature who *must* have been Lord Byron, since there was nobody or nothing else the stranger could be talking to—lay contentedly on his back, his short, pink legs circling lazily in the air, his snout quivering, and his piggish face gazing absentmindedly about him.

The two faces disappeared behind the fence. Quietly the eavesdroppers crept away from the scene and hurried off as quickly as their numb feet could take them, to tell the rest of the townsfolk what they had seen and heard.

"Sorcerers! Both of them!" they whispered as soon as they were certain they were well out of earshot. The boys wiped the sweat from their foreheads as they told everyone they met how lucky they were to have gotten away. Why, if that stranger, they shuddered, had *known* they had been there, why, they'd have had the devil himself to pay!

News of witchcraft whispered through the small river town. And while the rumors about him spread, Dan Rice leaned back against the fence, slapped his fat pink companion on his broad back, and rolled over and over, laughing to himself. That night, he laughed, when their show began, the town hall would be full—and so would Dan Rice's pockets. The performance he had just given for the couple of hayseeds on the other side of the fence guaranteed that!

Rice looked over at his friend. The pig's eyes were already shut, and his snores told Dan that Lord Byron was sound asleep. Dan leaned back against the fence, pushed the brim of his hat low over his forehead so it covered his eyes, and laughed once more.

As a teenager, Rice, an orphan boy, had ridden racehorses to one gold ribbon after another. He had loved horses and racing but, in 1842, when he was nineteen, he began to look for other adventures to enjoy.

Dan's new adventure began with a man named C. L. Kise. Kise, Dan was pleased to discover, traveled about the countryside looking for odd curiosities. When he found something exciting, he bought it as cheaply as possible. Then he set about finding a showman eager to make a fortune—and sold the oddity for as much as he could.

Kise boasted to Dan that he was the man who had brought the sailor with the mermaid to the greatest showman of them all, P. T. Barnum. Rice was impressed with Kise and his tales. He was even more impressed with one special curiosity the old collector showed him.

Rice took one long look at Kise's prize possession of the moment—Lord Byron, the "educated pig"—and the two of them struck a deal.

Rice and Lord Byron had been on the road together ever since.

By sundown the town hall was crowded with people who were eager to pay their money to see the educated pig and its crazy master. They didn't have long to wait.

The room had been full for only a few minutes when a little chin-whiskered fellow who, except for the twinkle in his eye, was a dead ringer for Uncle Sam, rushed into the room. Money was quickly scooped from outstretched hands, and in a few moments Dan Rice was performing trick after trick before a watchful audience.

He took thick iron bars and bent them as though they were pretzels. He scooped up a cannonball in both hands, tossed it high over his head, and then caught it neatly on the back of his neck. Between tricks, he danced about the room and sang ridiculous, funny songs.

Dan Rice performed one trick after another. He danced and sang and clowned, while the townspeople sat and stared and waited. Now and then a few of them laughed at a particularly funny tune or watched wide-eyed as Dan caught another cannonball and balanced it on the back of his neck. But everyone was restless. They had not come, hard-earned money in hand, to see some crazy stranger singing and dancing and doing strong-man's tricks. They had come to see his pig!

And at last the pig appeared. When Rice figured that he could not keep his audience in their seats any longer, he quickly retrieved Lord Byron from somewhere just outside the town-hall door. The spectators grumbled.

What they saw looked just like any other plain, ordinary, and not-too-intelligent pig. Why, it didn't look any better than its owner!

Then Rice set the pig down in the center of the room. The minute it touched the wooden floor, the pink creature began dancing and twirling on its hind feet. Lord Byron circled about several times, curtsied, and sat down.

Nobody said a word. Dan glanced at his pocket watch, looked about the room, and smiled. "Lord Byron," he asked, glancing down at his companion, "could you tell me the time?"

The pig stared over its snout at the people in the front row. Without dropping its eyes from them, it scratched eight times with its right foot on the hardwood floor. Then, with its left, it scratched ten more. A buzzing sound filled the room as the audience glanced down at their pocket watches and read the time—ten minutes after eight. The pig had scratched once with the right foot for each hour and once with the left for every minute! The crowd roared.

The noise stopped when Rice thanked the pig, reset his pocket watch, and taking a deck of cards from his pocket, spread them out in his hand. Dan asked Lord Byron to tell the audience what card he was about to pick from the deck. All the pig would have to do, Rice explained, winking at his audience, would be to scratch out the number of the card with either foot on the floor.

Turning his back to Lord Byron and holding the deck up so everyone but his companion could see, Rice slipped a five of hearts from the deck and showed it to the audience. Sliding it back into the deck, he turned again to the pig, which sat scratching absentmindedly at one ear with its hind foot. Lord Byron finished scratching, glanced up at the man alongside him, then scratched five times on the floor.

When the excited audience stopped shouting and clapping, Dan Rice went about the group, pausing here and there to ask the age of a young lady or an old farmer. No sooner was the answer whispered to Rice than Lord Byron began scratching out the right number in the center of the circle.

By the time Dan Rice and his curly tailed companion wrapped up their performance by singing a duet—Lord Byron coming in with low, snorting wails that sounded wonderfully like a stuck trumpet—the whole town knew they had seen a sight they would be talking about for a long time to come.

The two performers left that night on the evening train. If you had ridden out of town with them, Dan might have explained between bursts of laughter how simple it was for Lord Byron to act so smart. Rice might have shown you how, by rubbing his fingernail against a thumbnail, he made a sound too slight for his audience to hear but audible to Lord Byron. The pig would then repeat each sound by scratching its foot on the floor. Rice had other signs to tell the pig whether to use the right paw or the left, or whether to shake its head or grunt. The rest of the show depended upon Rice's—and his audience's—imagination.

The two companions traveled from town to town. Perhaps, after a while, Dan Rice became jealous of the pig's popularity. At any rate, one day they split up, and Rice joined a traveling puppet show. Standing out in front of the little portable theater, he joked with Judy, got hit on the head by Punch, and sang crazy songs that he made up as he went along. One day he met an old, gray-haired showman named Phineas Taylor, who asked him to be a strong man in his dime museum. Rice did so for a while and then, one afternoon, he mentioned that he was thinking of going East. The old showman told Rice to call on his nephew, a bright, spunky lad named after himself, he boasted. "Phineas Taylor Barnum" was the name the old man wrote on the letter of recommendation that he handed Rice. "The place to find P. T.," the old man said, "is at New York's American Museum."

Rice was astounded by the bustling activity of New York City. Crowds were everywhere. And the biggest ones, he discovered, were at the American Museum.

Barnum watched with unconcealed delight while Rice auditioned his tricks. Never one to resist making a good performance better, Barnum quickly set about restaging Rice's act. And under Barnum's direction, Dan Rice the Strong Man became the hit of the museum's five floors of curiosities and entertainments.

On opening night, half a dozen husky volunteers stepped up from the audience to help carry a 125-gallon barrel onto the stage. While Dan Rice lay on his back, the volunteers—carefully planted in the audience beforehand —lowered the huge container onto his hands and feet. The barrel tilted back and forth, water splashing from a hole high on its side.

Slowly Rice straightened his legs and arms, and the barrel rose high into the air. The six men returned to the center of the stage and strained to balance the enormous load among them as they carried it off the stage.

For four nights the act was a huge success. On the morning of the fifth performance, Rice asked for a raise.

Furious, Barnum refused. Rice did not ask again—he was too busy scheming. By that evening Rice knew exactly what he would do. He waited until the huge barrel was carried to the stage, water splashing over the shoulders of the six volunteers, and carefully lowered onto his waiting feet and hands. Then, after looking to make sure his whole audience was watching, he reached up and lifted the barrel overhead with one hand. Rice tipped it sideways so that everyone could see inside. The barrel was empty except for a five-gallon bucket of water that hung alongside the hole. It was from this smaller bucket that the water splashed out, making the huge barrel appear full.

The audience went wild with laughter. Everyone— that is, everyone except Barnum—thought Rice had played a great joke. But the next morning Barnum hammered a sign to the front of his museum.

Mr. Dan Rice, it announced in huge, bold letters, *in Consequence of a Temporary Indisposition, Will Not Appear at the American Museum Until Further Notice.*

Leaving the American Museum and Barnum behind, Rice joined a circus and became a clown. The crowds especially loved his ridiculous, mocking, and very funny songs. No one ever knew what Dan Rice would sing next. He made up his songs as he sang them, and they were always about people in the audience and in the ring. One evening in Buffalo, New York, one of the musicians in the circus band became enraged over a song Rice sang about him. The red-faced trumpet player left the tent that evening as soon as the performance was over.

The next morning he stormed into the hotel room where Rice was sound asleep. Never a man to pass up a

Dan Rice, the King of American Clowns

good fight, Rice leaped from bed, his fists swinging. He caught the intruder around the neck and was about to throw him out the open window when, reluctantly, he stopped. His hotel room, he realized, was on the fifth floor.

Instead, Dan hit the intruder several times over the head and threw him out the door. Locking it behind him, he went back to bed.

Rice did not give the fight another thought—that is, not until that evening, when a deputy sheriff stepped into the ring while Rice was performing. The band stopped playing in the middle of a song. Rice stopped, too, and tore open the envelope the sheriff handed him. He read its contents out loud to his audience. It was a warrant for his arrest.

"Ladies and gentlemen," Rice said when he had finished reading the warrant, "I don't see here where it says that the law has the right to deprive good citizens of seeing all the show they've paid to see. Sit down, sheriff, and enjoy yourself for the rest of the show. Laugh," he coaxed the officer. "Afterwards, I'll return and you can arrest me here in the circus ring. Isn't that right?" he asked, turning toward his audience.

The audience nearly went wild with approval, and the officer returned quietly to his seat.

Rice went back to his song and dance, and then the bareback riders and other acts swarmed into the ring. One after another the acts performed and then, in the solemn hush of the tent, the ringmaster strode to the center of the ring.

He removed his hat, bowed, and, standing as majestically as he could in a jacket two sizes too big, he spoke as eloquently as he knew how. "The piquant sauce of authority is ready and waiting," he said. "Yet the pudding of laughter, the pudding of wit, the pudding of fun cannot be served. The Rice," he shouted, "is gone!"

Leaping from his seat, the enraged sheriff charged for the exit, swearing he would find that clown—or else. Throughout the night, lanterns flickered beneath circus wagons, and the deputy's men poked inside every tent. Others watched every hotel. But nowhere was the clown to be found.

While the ringmaster had held everyone's attention in the ring, Rice had quietly slipped into a borrowed jacket and cap, dirtied his face and hands with mud, and joined the roustabouts playing cards outside the big tent. He flopped down on one of their cots during the night, cap pushed over his face, and before dawn had brightened the street, he had sneaked aboard a baker's wagon parked outside a nearby hotel. Inside the wagon, he had ridden through the sleeping streets, munching on fresh bread and biscuits. When the driver reached the restaurant farthest from the showgrounds, Rice quietly slipped away. He walked a short distance and then caught a ride with a farmer on his way home from market. Other farmers' wagons took him to a riverside town some twenty miles away, where he climbed aboard a steamer.

The circus folded its tents without him and moved on to the next town. But the story of Dan Rice, the clown who had outwitted the sheriff, arrived before the circus. When the show began without him, the audience demanded Rice. Bareback riders, camels, elephants . . . nothing but the famous clown would appease the crowd.

Somehow the circus owners managed to find the runaway and to settle matters with the ruffled deputy sheriff. The next evening the show opened. Rice, dressed in gray convict clothes studded with stars, was led into the ring by a clown in a police uniform and with a gun tucked under his arm. Rice's hands were shackled, and he dragged a ball and chain from one leg. The "officer" unlocked the handcuffs, removed the ball and chain, and Dan Rice began his act to wild applause.

Traveling with various circuses, Rice played packed houses from Texas to New England. One day he won a circus of his very own. It all happened because Dan's partner told him that Dan's share of the profits from their riverboat circus was gone. The two men argued and finally decided to settle their differences over a deck of cards. Dan and his partner sat down to a game of poker. While their boat floated down the Ohio River, the chandelier swaying overhead and the paddlewheel churning, Dan Rice won the card game—and with it, the whole circus.

It was this circus—"Dan Rice's Great Show"—that traveled the Mississippi in its big riverboat and performed at countless riverside towns. And it was this circus that the five young Ringling brothers watched steaming up the river one morning and never forgot—not even when they themselves were the proud owners of the "Biggest and Greatest Show on Earth."

It is said that Mark Twain wrote about Rice's circus in *The Adventures of Huckleberry Finn:*

> It was the splendidest sight that ever was, when they all come riding in, two by two, gentleman and lady, side by side . . . aweaving around the ring so gentle and graceful . . . faster and faster they went . . . the horses leaning more and more, and the ringmaster going round and round the center pole, cracking his whip and shouting "Hi! hi!" and the clowns cracking jokes behind him.

Always, Dan Rice was cracking jokes.

Eight cream-colored horses drew his circus's red-and-gold bandwagon. In front of, around, and behind it came more horses and camels, elephants and a grizzly bear, leopards, panthers, wolves, plus an alligator and an ostrich.

Rice took an elephant, put it in a clown costumer, and taught it to walk the tightrope. And then he taught an old rhino to do tricks that would have made Lord Byron look like a dunce.

At the close of the circus, the tent would glow with red, green, blue, and purple light and glittering showers of sparks from a huge chandelier suspended from the top of the canvas. Below, riders would circle round and round the ring in their colorful costumes while the band played on and on. But what the crowd always remembered long after the riverboat had disappeared round the far bend was that wildly funny and unforgettable clown, Dan Rice.

When he was young, Ehrich Weiss knew that someday he would be famous for performing "miracles" that no one else had ever dreamed of. Like Houdin, the magician Ehrich idolized and whose name he finally took for his own, Houdini was slight and painfully shy. And, like his hero, he became a master at manipulating others' imaginations. Lesser magicians worked with pigeons and rabbits; Houdini made an elephant disappear. Baffled crowds who saw him escape from locks and chains swore he had to be able to shrink his bones to perform such feats.

Houdini

No performer ever faced a tougher audience.

It was late afternoon, but the gray, overcast sky was as dull as early morning. Wind whipped across the tugboat's deck. Somewhere a foghorn sounded. Aboard the tug, a group of shivering reporters gathered around a strange-looking box and the little man who said his name was Houdini.

"Here!" As he spoke, the small man with the peculiar name tossed something to one of the newsmen. The reporter caught it in two gloved hands. It was early spring and cold enough for the journalists to be warmly dressed, but this unusual man who had brought them out into the middle of New York Harbor wore only a cotton swimming suit. His long hair was gray, but his body looked strong and powerful.

"Take a good look at those," he said, nodding toward the handcuffs in the reporter's hands. "Make sure they're the real thing and then pass them on to your friends."

"You!" He pointed to a fat, baldheaded newsman who was trying unsuccessfully to light a cigar in the fierce wind. "Look over these leg irons. Don't hand them around until you're sure they'll hold."

Then, motioning for the others to follow him, Houdini strolled over to the odd-looking box. His walk was fast, restless. He bounced on the balls of his feet as if he had too much energy to stay on the ground for long. "The rest of you boys examine this packing crate." He nudged it with his foot. "And don't forget to look at this lid, too."

"Excuse me, Mr. Houdini," interrupted one of the reporters. The young man in a tweed top coat with the collar turned up against the wind stepped up to Houdini with pad and pencil in hand and asked, "What exactly are you going to do?"

Houdini turned and smiled at the reporter, who wasn't much taller than he was. "First," he said, "you and your friends are going to put those cuffs on me. Then the leg irons."

The reporter nodded as he made notes in his little book.

"Next, you're going to help me climb into this box," Houdini continued.

Again the young man nodded, as he turned to another page.

"Then, you're going to nail the lid on good and tight."

The reporter was writing as fast as he could.

"Then you toss the box and me in the harbor."

The young man stopped writing. His face grew pale. He stared at the serious-looking little man in the swimming trunks.

"What are you going to do then, Mr. Houdini?" he asked.

Houdini smiled. "I'm going to get out. Wouldn't you?"

The reporters weren't sorry that they had climbed aboard this tug and ridden out into the middle of New York Harbor. They had met a lot of people and seen a lot of unbelievable things in their days; but they had never seen anything like this man who called himself Houdini.

They took their time examining the packing crate. It was almost square in shape and just large enough to hold a man who was sitting down. Its sides were made of thick boards, each apparently fastened to the others with long screws. The box was weighted down with lengths of heavy iron pipe, which were fastened to the sides so that the crate would sink. The lid, as solid as the rest of the box, lay alongside the big case.

Nobody can be as suspicious as a big-city reporter—or as nosey. Each man carefully examined the box and its top. The newsmen tapped, kicked, and tugged on every board. They ran their fingers along the edges and groped about the corners of the crate—just to make sure everything was as it was supposed to be. As far as they could tell, the box was escape-proof.

The handcuffs and the leg irons were examined as closely as the crate. They, too, seemed tough and unbreakable.

When the last reporter was satisfied, Houdini held out his arms and was handcuffed by the newspapermen. Others securely fastened the leg irons to his ankles. Then, with the reporters' help, the little man climbed inside the crate.

Houdini's manager handed out hammers and nails to the reporters. Half a dozen of them nailed the lid tightly to the case.

Meanwhile, others wrapped a long length of thick rope

around the bottom, top, and four sides of the box, bringing the ends of the rope together and tying them securely on top.

A large crane was swung over the crate; its hook was carefully lowered and slipped under the taut rope. At a signal from Houdini's manager, the odd box was lifted over the side of the tug. It swung slowly back and forth over the deep water.

On a muffled signal from Houdini, the box was slowly lowered. There was a splash and several ripples, and then the box disappeared. Only the ripples and the long length of rope pointed toward where the crate had vanished into the murky water.

Wind whistled across the deck of the tug, stung the reporters' faces and hands, and then suddenly was gone. The ticking of a dozen watches was almost audible as the twelve reporters stared at the sweeping second hands, the silent water, and back again at the second hands.

There was a ripple and what looked for a moment like a hand. But it was only a sea gull that had swooped down on the water, splashed, and then flown off again. Half a minute went by. Forty seconds. Still there was no sign of Houdini. Someone coughed. Someone else looked nervously up at the crane and wondered out loud if, perhaps, they shouldn't pull the box up. Now!

Fifty-five seconds. Twelve restless reporters crowded about the deck. Then, at fifty-seven seconds, an arm *did* break through the water. An instant later, Houdini shook his head free, pushed the long, damp hair from his eyes, and glanced about for the tug.

A shout went up from on board. Houdini swam in its direction as a dozen hands reached out for him. Together, the reporters hauled him aboard.

The little man in the swimming trunks leaned against the railing, smiled, and caught his breath, while his manager gave the signal to haul the almost-forgotten box aboard.

Once the crate landed on the deck, hammers were again handed to the men. The reporters ripped open the top of the box. Inside were the opened handcuffs and leg irons.

The man who called himself Houdini was only nine years old on the morning in 1883 when Jack Heffler's circus rolled into Appleton, Wisconsin. Everyone still called the boy Ehrich and knew him as one of the Weiss children from a family of immigrants only recently arrived in America. The boy had not yet learned to escape from handcuffs or packing crates. He had still to discover the book that would inspire him and provide him with the name by which he would be known all over the world. But already Ehrich had convinced the owner of this small circus that it would pay to have a local boy on the bill. Neighbors came from all around to watch "Eric, the Prince of the Air" walk on a rope in a set of long, red woolen underwear.

The rope was only a few feet off the ground. And the underwear was hot and scratchy. But that day Ehrich would not have traded places with anyone he could imagine. If he had been asked to, Ehrich Weiss would have traveled out of town with the circus. But no such request was made, and when the circus folded its tent and rolled out of town, Ehrich's father made sure that the boy stayed behind. The long underwear was put away in a drawer until winter, and Ehrich went back to selling papers and shining shoes.

Then, just before summer was over, Ehrich's father took him to Milwaukee. There the boy saw a famous magician, Harry Kellar. Kellar changed water to wine and back to water again. He made a fully grown rosebush suddenly blossom out of nowhere. And he made a "genuine" princess float in mid-air! But to Ehrich, Kellar's rope ties were the most miraculous wonders of all.

Kellar asked for volunteers to come onstage and tie his hands behind his back. But as soon as a knot was tightened, Kellar would suddenly tap the unsuspecting volunteer on the shoulder with a free hand. Then he would turn around so that the volunteer and the audience could see that his hands were still tied. Tied, untied, tied again . . . it happened so *fast* that, to Ehrich, it almost seemed that a third hand miraculously appeared. And all the while, to the delight of everyone in the audience, Kellar looked about with an amused innocence, as though he had nothing whatever to do with this uncanny occurrence. All the way home, Kellar's challenge to "tie my wrists together so that I cannot release myself" rang in Ehrich's ears.

By the time he crawled into bed that night, Ehrich had made up his mind. No longer would he be simply Eric, Prince of the Air. From that time on he was Eric the Great. The next day the boy challenged everyone who would listen to tie him up and watch him wiggle his way loose. The fact that all too often he didn't succeed didn't bother him in the least. Ehrich gave up selling papers and shining shoes. There was no future in either, he said. Instead, he found a job hauling trunks about for a luggage shop. There he could spend his free moments studying different kinds of locks. The first chance he had, Ehrich apprenticed himself to a locksmith. In his new job he learned how the notches in a key turned the mechanism of a lock. His proudest possession became a piece of bent wire that went everywhere he did. He slipped the wire into every new lock he passed. Continually he changed its shape to make it more and more adaptable.

When Ehrich was thirteen, his family suddenly packed and went off to New York City. There Ehrich found himself a job as a tie cutter in a necktie factory, a dog-eared deck of playing cards in his hip pocket. His free moments were spent practicing card tricks as well as rope ties and escapes. A friend, Jack Hayman, a co-worker in the tie factory, was an amateur magician, too. One day Jack lent Ehrich a book that explained how to get out of knotted ropes, cleverly hinged boxes, and even a sack whose drawstrings were pulled tight, knotted, and sealed.

Hoping to find other such books, Ehrich rummaged through one second-hand bookstore after another. In one he found an old work entitled *The Memoirs of Robert Houdin, Ambassador, Author and Conjurer*.

Ehrich spent most of the night reading about this magician—who also had stumbled upon a book of magic. By morning Ehrich knew he had found his idol. When he told his friend about his discovery, Hayman suggested that Ehrich change his name to Houdini.

Ehrich thought about what his friend had said. He thought about the book he had just read, and about Harry Kellar, the magician he had seen in Milwaukee. Then he made up his mind. "From now on," he told Hayman, "the world will call me Harry Houdini."

Harry, assisted by his brother Theo, performed his magic at clubs and parties or wherever he could convince somebody to let him do his tricks. Harry was not always successful. Most people expected a magician to be tall and grand and impressive. Houdini was only a little more than five feet tall. He was nervous, and his voice sounded frightened—when it could be heard at all. He knew a lot of tricks, but he did them with such a serious, half-frightened look that most of their wonder was lost.

Harry and his brother jammed their show with something for everyone. They did card tricks, handcuff releases, and a trunk escape using a trick box they had managed to buy from a starving magician. Harry and Theo would haul the trunk to the center of the stage. Harry, his hands bound behind his back, would climb inside. Theo would snap the trunk shut and wrap it with thick rope. Then he pulled a screen around the trunk and ducked behind it. The very second that Theo disappeared behind the screen, Houdini's head suddenly reappeared. Houdini stepped out from behind the screen, and holding his freed hands high for everyone to see, he would fling the screen aside to reveal the trunk still locked and bound. Quickly, but with great effort, he would untie the ropes. As the lid was lifted, Theo would step from the trunk, turning as he did, so the audience could see that his hands were firmly bound behind his back with the same tapes that moments earlier had held his brother.

The highlight of 1893 was Chicago's World's Fair. Houdini went to Chicago, hoping to further his fame and fortune in the bright lights and commotion of the fair. Harry found a job in Kohl & Middleton's Museum, where spectators eagerly paid ten cents to see freaks, sword swallowers, fire-eaters, jugglers, acrobats, contortionists —and Harry Houdini. Houdini gave twenty shows a day in what the banner proclaimed was the "Hall of Freaks and Miracle Workers." Between acts he would run downstairs to perform other stunts in the theater below. What free moments Houdini had left were spent talking with the other performers. He became good friends with the sword swallowers, the fire-eaters, and the rubber men. Houdini learned all that he could learn about their tricks, and in doing so he became convinced that practically any feat was possible, once its secret was known.

Houdini liked working at Kohl & Middleton's. The crowds were large and happy, and if the pay was small, at least it was regular. But Kohl & Middleton's policy demanded frequent changes of program, and soon the Houdini's found themselves standing outside the museum with nothing but their ex-employer's promise that "someday soon" they would be called back. Houdini and Theo performed in other dime museums, music halls, carnivals, traveling medicine shows, on street corners—wherever it looked as though a crowd might pay them to perform.

The next year, the Brothers Houdini found themselves back in New York City and performing magic at Coney Island. One of the other acts at the amusement park was the Floral Sisters, a group of singers and dancers. Houdini began spending the time between shows with one of the sisters, Bess. One afternoon the two of them finished off a day spent exploring the wonders of Coney Island by getting married. Theo went on to work his act alone, and little Bess, who weighed only ninety pounds, took his place in the trunk.

That fall, Harry and Bess set out on the road. They worked one-night stands wherever they happened to find themselves each evening. In the afternoons they would hang up posters and wait, hoping the townspeople would

fill the hall or room they had rented for their performance. Harry did some card tricks and made silk handkerchiefs appear . . . and disappear. He asked for volunteers
to come up and examine the trunk. He told them to tie
his hands behind his back and then to lift him into a
large sack. The volunteers drew the mouth of the sack
tight, knotted it, and sealed it. Then the sack and Houdini were placed inside the trunk, the lid was shut and
locked, and the whole trunk was roped and sealed.

Bess took her place between the curtains, holding one
fold in each hand. "Ladies and gentlemen," she would
say "you've seen Houdini's wrists bound behind his back
and seen him sealed inside the sack. You see the locked,
roped trunk with Houdini inside. And you see me on the
outside.

"I'll clap my hands three times," Bess would say, slowly
drawing the curtains. And then, you . . . ladies and gentlemen . . . watch. One . . . two . . . three," she said, as her
tiny hands clapped together. On the last clap, the curtains closed, and Bess disappeared behind them. Just as
suddenly they were flung wide as Houdini stepped out
and bowed. With the help of the volunteers, Houdini,
his jacket off and his shirt sleeves rolled up, untied and
unlocked the trunk. The bag was quickly opened; from
it stepped Bess. Her hands were bound behind her. She
wore Houdini's coat.

Night after night the Houdinis ran through their act,
each time ending their performance with the trunk
escape. Always it was the last trick that won the greatest
applause.

When the Houdinis found themselves back at Kohl
& Middleton's in Chicago, Harry visited police headquarters, where Bess, according to Harry's instructions,

caught the eye of Lieutenant Andy Rohan, the huge, red-handlebar-moustached chief of detectives. Bess engaged the chief in a rather lengthy conversation, and Houdini, meanwhile, wandered off to have a look at the locks on the jail cells. They looked tougher than Harry had imagined, and the next afternoon he and his wife paid another call on the Irish detective. By this time suspicious, the lieutenant told them he was too busy to talk. But the couple stayed long enough so that, later that day, a confident Houdini met with some of his reporter friends to tell them casually, "If I were handcuffed and locked in a cell in this city's jail, I'd be out in no time."

As Harry expected, the newsmen were not likely to let a good story slip through their hands. Together they took off for Rohan's office. When the red-faced detective heard what Houdini had been telling the reporters, he was happy to handcuff Harry and lock him in a cell. But no one was impressed when fifteen minutes later Houdini stepped back into Rohan's office, the open handcuffs in his hands.

"Go on," one of the reporters said, "you probably have a pocketful of keys. Andy's been telling us how you've been hanging around here."

This time it was Houdini's turn to get angry. "All right," he answered, "if that's what you think, you take my clothes, search me, and lock me up again."

They did so, locking him in one cell and his clothes in another.

None of them said a word when ten minutes later Houdini sauntered in, fully dressed, through the jail's front door.

That night and the next morning the papers played the story up with big, bold headlines. From then on, every time Houdini found himself in a new city, he always set out to find the local jail. Before long, police officials throughout the country were declaring their relief that Houdini had not decided on a life of crime. "As a criminal," they all agreed, "he'd have been difficult to catch and impossible to hold."

England's Scotland Yard had declared that no man could ever escape from its cells. The superintendent of the world-famous police force handcuffed Houdini, and before the superintendent could turn around, the Escape King was free. In Holland, Houdini chained himself to the arm of a windmill. In Russia, he escaped from a Siberian prison van, an "impenetrable" steel cell on wheels. Back in the United States, he escaped from an enormous leather football, tightly laced together by experts, and also from an iron boiler and a zinc-lined piano box. Hanging suspended head downward from a skyscraper, Houdini worked himself free of a strait jacket.

No one ever knew what to expect when he went to see Houdini. One evening the escape artist announced to his audience that he had learned how to walk through a solid brick wall. He motioned toward a huge pile of bricks stacked in a corner of the stage and explained that during that night's show several volunteer bricklayers would build a wall on the stage. When they were finished, he said, he would walk through the wall.

As soon as Houdini completed his announcement, several volunteers came up from the audience and began building the wall. They built it on top of a steel beam that was raised an inch or two off the ground on casters, so that the wall could be moved around on the stage when it was finished.

Houdini, the Escape King

Houdini, meanwhile, bowed and went on with his performance.

When the wall was finished, he asked for members of the audience to come up and examine it closely. Houdini also invited them to inspect the rug that covered the middle of the stage. To erase any doubts anyone might still have about the rug, he then passed around a large sheet of muslin for the volunteers to examine. When they had done so, he spread the sheet out over the rug.

Assistants pushed the eight-foot-high brick wall into position on the center of the rug, perpendicular to the proscenium. Low folding screens were placed on both sides of the middle section of the wall. Houdini pointed out to the members of the audience that they could all see the top of the wall. Then he positioned the spectators on the stage so that all of them were standing on the rug and facing the wall. Everyone on stage could see both ends of the wall. It would be impossible for Houdini to try to climb over the wall or step around it without being seen.

As the orchestra began to play, Houdini stepped behind one of the screens. "I'm here," he shouted over the deafening music, holding a hand high so everyone could tell for certain where he was.

"And . . . now . . . ," he called, his hand disappearing beneath the screen, "I'm *here!*" The showman's hand shot up again, this time on the other side of the wall.

Sweeping the screen aside, Houdini stepped forward to take a bow.

The secret of this trick, as of most of Houdini's stunts, was really very simple. Concealed beneath the rug was a trap door. When an assistant opened the door from below, the rug sagged just enough for Houdini to squeeze under the wall. The members of the audience who had been pressed into "guarding" Houdini actually made his escape possible by keeping the rug taut enough so that the trap door was never detected.

For more than a quarter of a century, Houdini's name appeared on theater marquees and in newspaper headlines all over the world. Again and again the daring hero met his audience's challenges—and won. With every performance Houdini fought against great risks to keep the fame that he had won with such great effort and determination. He knew that courage had to be practiced. And he practiced it—every day of his life.

Whitey Dukinfield ran away from home when he was eleven and spent the rest of his years juggling and joking his way through life and escaping the humdrum. Runaway, juggler, vaudevillian, and movie star, he was a bluff who pretended to be mean; he was a fraud whose pretensions always turned out to be funny.

W. C. Fields

WHITEY sat in the darkened auditorium watching two brothers juggle half a dozen lemons on the brightly lighted stage.

His real name wasn't Whitey. It was William Claude Dukinfield. But the boy with the pale blonde hair did not like his long name—not one bit.

The only good thing about his name was that usually nobody ever called him by it—nobody, that is, except his folks. At least they shortened it to Claude—though, when Whitey stopped to think about it, "Claude" was even worse.

The boy did not mind too much when his mother called him Claude. He liked his mother, and she usually called to tell him something good. But when the boy's father shouted, "Claude!" it was almost always so that he could box Whitey behind the ears.

Whitey was eleven in 1890 and older than his two brothers and two sisters. "We're all poor," he would remind them. "But *I* was poor first." It was up to Whitey to try to help his father earn money for the family.

That was not an easy job. Whitey's father was a sales-man—who seldom sold anything. Fortunately for the Dukinfield family, James Dukinfield dealt in fruits and vegetables. The family could always eat—even if their only fare was the same old fruits and vegetables no one else wanted.

Whitey helped his father load up the cart each morn-ing. And he tried to keep their scrawny old nag of a horse stumbling forward instead of falling over sideways. He had to keep his father awake—some of the time—and the fruits and vegetables out of the greedy hands of school-boys who tried snitching them when no one was looking.

These things he did because he had to. But the work that he liked most was calling out the names of every fruit and vegetable that came to his mind. Unfortu-nately, the zeal with which he performed this part of his job occasionally got him into trouble.

His attention wandering from the jugglers on the stage, Whitey remembered that he was in trouble at that very moment. He began to daydream about the events of the preceding day that had led up to his pre-dicament. Blocking out the sound of the piano that ac-companied the juggling act, Whitey could still hear his own voice echoing through the narrow streets of Phila-delphia as he called out the names of assorted fruits and vegetables. He could hear how good he had been at mock-ing his father's queer nasal voice and the accent that told everyone that James Dukinfield came from London.

"Calabashes!" Whitey remembered singing out, laugh-ing at the ridiculous sound of the name and glancing over at his father to make certain that he was still asleep.

"Pomegranates!" he hollered.

"And rutabagas!"

Again and again he yelled, repeating the commotion on each new block. Every time he sang them out, the words sounded crazier and more ridiculous than before. Soon he was laughing so hard he could hardly shout.

But he did. And while he sat there, urging the old nag forward, and while he shouted and laughed and listened with one ear to his father's snoring, Whitey racked his brain to think of other queer-sounding names.

"Persimmons!" he called out. It didn't bother him that neither he nor his father had seen or smelled or touched any of these fruits and vegetables for weeks, or even months.

It was the queer-sounding names he cared about—not the things they belonged to. And the funnier those names sounded, the louder Whitey shouted them.

"Calabashes!" he sang out again as the horse tumbled into the shade of another block.

He was just deciding between "Cauliflowers!" and "Bilberries!" when a window flew open above him. A fat lady stuck her head out, shaking a mop of scraggly hair at him.

"Calabashes?" She hurled the word back at him, a dubious squint on her pinched face.

"Calabashes!" The word tickled his tongue as he called it out again. "Fresh, fresh calabashes!"

The mop-headed woman ducked back inside and the window slammed shut. Moments later she came bursting out the door.

Whitey tried to get the old horse moving. But it was too late.

"But you said . . ." she screamed when Whitey tried to explain that they had nothing but apples and tomatoes for sale that day.

James Dukinfield blinked from the angry woman to the boy. His red face twisted into an unconvincing smile.

"My boy," he muttered, chuckling and whacking Whitey alongside his left ear, "he's new on the job."

The sour-faced housewife only glared. "I'm sorry. Sorry," Mr. Dukinfield said, grinning at the woman and cuffing the boy again for good measure. "But we sold the last, ah, calabashes, wasn't it . . . hmm, yes . . . on the very last block."

Grabbing the reins from Whitey, Mr. Dukinfield sent the old horse flying. With his free hand he tipped his cap at the lady and then whacked the boy again.

As soon as they were out of earshot of any potential customers, Mr. Dukinfield began to beat his son in earnest. He continued the punishment—at intervals—until late that evening— when Whitey had the good sense to disappear.

Still, Whitey thought, awakening from his daydream to the antics of the jugglers, he was almost glad the trouble had occurred. If he had to be in hiding, what better place to pick than the theater where these fabulous entertainers were performing? Rubbing his still-sore shoulders, Whitey watched the brothers toss more lemons, one after another, into the air. Not once did they drop even one.

The cool March winds had blown away when Whitey finally left the theater, and the air was sunny and warm. But the boy didn't notice. He was too busy juggling— magnificently—imaginary pomegranates and pears.

It was amazing how good he had become at juggling these imaginary objects. Like the entertainers he had just seen, Whitey never missed. Not once.

When the boy reached his house, he looked about carefully, but his father was nowhere in sight. The cart was there, though—full from another unsuccessful day. Full!

Quietly, Whitey stepped up to the cart. Cautiously, he reached inside and filled his arms with fruit. Then he ducked inside the stable. There he tossed a tomato into the air—just as he had juggled imaginary kumquats and parsnips. Only the tomato plopped, squashed, on the ground.

He tossed another. It, too, plopped—and was squashed.

Again and again he tried to juggle, pausing only long enough to make one trip after another to the cart. Tomatoes, lemons, apples, pears—Whitey had no idea how many fruits and vegetables he tossed in the air—and lost.

But his father did the next morning and Whitey got another beating.

"Forty dollars' worth! Ruined!" James Dukinfield shouted. He pressed his stinging hands together and glared at his oldest son. "Now what do you think of that?"

Whitey tried very hard *not* to think of how sore his bottom felt. He thought instead about running away. Running somewhere, anywhere his father would not be able to catch him. But he couldn't very well tell his father *that*. So he bit his lip and said nothing.

Whitey got into even more trouble. This time it wasn't over a tossed salad that he had snitched from his father's cart. Whitey had become pretty good at juggling. Half a dozen oranges lasted him most of the night. This time the trouble was due to a shovel.

Whitey had left a shovel lying in the yard. That

wouldn't have been so bad. But the shovel happened to be lying directly in James Dukinfield's path. Even that would have been only terrible. What made it horrible was that, when Whitey's father stepped on one end of the shovel, the other flipped up and whacked him on the knee.

Mr. Dukinfield yelled. He swore. And, hopping about on one leg, he chased Whitey with the shovel. He finally caught the boy and bounced the shovel off his head.

Again Whitey took to hiding. This time he decided he really would run away. But first, the boy found a big, heavy crate and carried it up into the stable's loft. He sat up there, holding the box in his lap and waiting.

After a long while Whitey heard the stable door open below. He leaned forward and looked down. His father had stopped directly below the place where Whitey was sitting. Whitey let go of the box.

The crate landed squarely on James Dukinfield's head. Whitey waited just long enough to hear his father yell. Then, satisfied that he had finally gotten even for all his beatings, he jumped down from the loft, and dashed out the door.

A mile or so down the road Whitey stopped running. He caught his breath and then scrambled off to the side of the road. Pushing the bushes aside, he made his way into a thicket. On hands and knees he crawled through a big tangle of shrubs and worked his way down into a dugout that he and his friends had covered with old boards and branches several summers before. The dugout was a regular meeting place, and several of Whitey's friends were already there.

Whitey was beginning to have second thoughts about running away. He was nervous, too, about having hit his father with that crate. The farther he had run, the more misgivings he had had. He was almost ready to go back and take the whipping he knew would be waiting.

But when he told his friends what he had done, the envy on their dirty faces soon put everything back in a warm and proper perspective. He felt proud of himself indeed as his friends slapped him on the back. The old hole in the ground was full of laughter, and Whitey felt fine—until dinner time. Then the other boys went home.

The dugout was suddenly quiet and damp and cold. Of course, after dinner some of the boys sneaked back, bringing Whitey odds and ends from their meals. One fellow brought him a bun with butter and jam. Another had smuggled some pieces of parsnip—the one thing on his plate, Whitey was convinced, he hadn't liked. Another, who from the looks of him, liked everything on everyone's plate, brought Whitey a blanket borrowed from a neighbor's clothesline.

The blanket didn't ease Whitey's hunger. But that night it turned out to be the best treasure of all. By morning Whitey had decided that a dark, damp, cold hole in the mud was not exactly the best place to call home. He stayed for a couple of weeks. But his friends began to tire of snitching food for him. And rains were turning the dugout into a pond. And so a dingy-looking Whitey set out to find himself some new headquarters.

He settled at first for a barrel. It, at least, was dry. But it was also cramped. A few days later he moved into a packing crate. It had plenty of room—and plenty of sharp nails in all the wrong places.

Spying an open basement window one evening, Whitey quietly turned someone's warm, empty cellar into a bedroom of his own. At least in the dark he thought the cellar was empty. When morning came, Whitey discovered that its shelves were stocked with jars of jam. Each night, Whitey crept into the cellar. Each night he made himself comfortable—and opened another jar. Mornings he crept away, before anyone else was awake.

Then one night he found the window shut and sealed. The owner must have discovered the empty jam jars tucked away behind the full ones. Sadder but wiser, Whitey set out to find himself another hideaway. Never again would he let greed ruin such a good thing.

By this time, Whitey had roamed far from his old neighborhood in search of warmer and cozier spots. The boys he ran into were strangers. Worse, they did not like the kid with the pale blonde hair who never had to go to school or home. Whitey's nose, which had grown sore and red from the cold, became an irresistible target for the fists of bullies everywhere. Whitey learned to keep an eye out for stray fists—as he used to watch from his father's wagon for schoolboys' greedy hands.

For a while, the runaway held a job selling newspapers on a street corner in downtown Philadelphia. Each morning he would pick up one of his papers, and sitting down on the rest of the pile, he would look for names as funny as calabashes and rutabagas. He always found them.

Then he would hurry off to his corner, folding the papers as he went and juggling half a dozen of them in the air.

"Isabel Schimmelpennick!" he would shout, "buys a new license for her dog!" He cried out his news with all the enthusiasm and conviction that less talented newsboys wasted on spectacular fires and shipwrecks. The passersby, amused and perplexed by the strange tales

they heard about Hermonius Glunk or Archibald Cad-
evens, paused to listen and went away reading one of
Whitey's papers.

Whitey enjoyed his work and prospered as a newsboy.
But spring was coming, and he set about looking for
some way to beat the heat.

He found what he was looking for in his paper. "Gomer
Wheatley," he read, "wants someone to help on an ice
wagon for a few hours."

It was hard to resist the temptation to shout out the
name of Gomer Wheatley for all the world to hear. But
Whitey succeeded. He wanted to save Gomer's job for
himself. As soon as he had sold the last paper in his pile,
Whitey took off to see Mr. Wheatley.

"Yes, the position is still available," the man with the
ice-blue eyes told the blonde-haired boy. "The job is a
cool one, and the day is over early."

It wasn't until later that Whitey realized why Gomer
Wheatley had not told him the *reason* the day was over
so early: Mr. Wheatley and he began their work in the
middle of the night! But the boy was too pleased to have
his afternoons to himself to care if he ever slept at all.
And so the next morning at three o'clock, Whitey found
himself fumbling about in the cool darkness, a heavy
cake of ice on his back. The night air was fresh and the
ice, cool. The only sound was that of the horse's hooves
clomping lazily along the darkened street. Dawn came,
and morning, and soon Whitey was on his way home. He
had nothing more to do except look around for something
to juggle.

He found tennis balls lying forgotten outside tennis
courts. He stopped to beg cigar boxes from shopkeepers.

With the money from his new job, Whitey found himself a room where he could juggle all day and night. He couldn't have been happier.

Then fall finally came, and everyone who had wanted ice so badly in July was now more interested in firewood. Again Whitey found himself out in the cold, hungry, and without a job.

There was only one thing to do. Swallowing his pride and hoping that none of his pals would see him, Whitey went to visit his grandmother.

He liked visiting her. She was old, but nice. And for the first time since he had run away, Whitey had more food than he could eat. Mornings and afternoons were spent happily juggling in her backyard. And then, suddenly, it all ended.

Whitey's grandmother got him a job. Before he knew what was happening, the boy found himself scrubbed, combed, and walking about in a clerk's apron in a department store.

His job, Whitey discovered when he regained his senses, was to carry change from one department to another. He was miserable. It was all he could do to walk past a door with all that money jingling in his pockets and not run out with it. And to top it all off, he was sure that any minute his old friends would see him. It was too much.

Before the week was over, Whitey fled the department store—without the money. He slipped away from his grandmother's to take a more satisfying job racking balls in a pool hall. The food wasn't nearly so good, but there were plenty of pool balls to juggle. And when Whitey got tired, there were empty pool tables to stretch out on.

Here, at last, was the perfect place, he thought. Whitey

was very well satisfied until one of the other boys who worked around the hall—a short little kid with bright-red hair—told him, "There's a new amusement park going up." Watching Whitey juggle half a dozen pool balls and an orange, he continued, "Why don't you see if you can get a job there?"

Whitey gave the lad a bored look and tossed another ball into the air. But the next morning he went straight to the park.

The owner was easy to pick out by the size and smell of his cigar. Before he could take it out of his mouth and tell the boy to scram, Whitey was juggling five tennis balls, all the while pretending that one of them was about to get away and then just managing to catch it as it flew off. The owner stood puffing on his cigar. The kid could juggle, he thought, and was funny besides. The owner had never seen anyone quite like Whitey.

"See that stuff all the time," he told Whitey when he had stopped juggling. "All that fancy tossing of yours is a dime a dozen. Still," he said, taking another puff on his cigar, "still, I like you. I'll give you a break. You've got a week to practice with the pros."

"What's the salary?" Whitey asked.

Coughing, the owner seemed suddenly aware of an emergency in the next room. "That's right," he mumbled, as he disappeared out the door. "Do a good job now and, ah, payday's not until next week."

Something in the way the new boy juggled caught the eye of the crowd. He was good. But there was more to his appeal than that. He had a funny way of seeming to be about to lose a ball and then somehow managing to snatch it back at the last moment. He caught it without even seeming to try, as if he were stunned that it had gotten away at all.

There was the way, too, that he kept putting the same three hats back on top of his head, only to knock them off again. He would spin about in time to see them tumbling—almost—to the floor. All of these stunts and the mad, hopelessly confused look on Whitey's face were things that the crowds found as wonderful as his juggling. Day after day Whitey juggled. His week was over before he knew it.

"You were fine, my boy, just fine," the owner said, glancing down at his newest performer.

Whitey stared back, nervously noting that there wasn't a trace of money in either of the owner's hands.

"Yes, sir," the owner said, pausing and glancing up at the ceiling. "It's just too bad."

"Too bad?" Whitey could feel his hungry stomach turning over.

"About the crowds," the owner mumbled.

"Oh, we were crowded," Whitey said, forcing a smile. "The crowds got bigger every day."

"Yep. It's just too bad that even with all those crowds . . ." the owner shook his head.

"And money," Whitey added nervously.

"And money . . ." the owner sighed.

"Yes?"

"That business was so *bad*," the owner moaned.

"Bad?" Whitey asked in disbelief.

"Terrible," came the reply.

Whitey blinked, overcome by the illogic of it all.

"But that's not your problem, is it, son?" the owner went on. Glancing at Whitey out of the corner of his eye, he slipped a handful of bills from his coat pocket and spread them in his hand.

"Let's see," he muttered, stalling and stealing another half look at the boy, "five dollars for the week." Again, he squinted at Whitey with half-closed eyes. "Less, of course, a dollar and a half. For agent's fee," he added quickly. "There you go, my boy. Three dollars . . . and a half."

Whitey Dukinfield stuffed the bills and loose change into his pocket and hurried for the door. Outside he quickly figured in his head that, taking out for meals and carfare, he was losing only a dime a week with his new job. A dime, he told himself, as he hurried off whistling, was a small price for being a juggler.

Not all of the people who worked for the cigar-smoking owner were so content with their wages. Two brothers who operated a teeterboard fought daily with the man. One evening they told Whitey they had had enough. "That's it," they said, "we're leaving in the morning."

"Where are you going?" Whitey asked.

"We're off to Atlantic City," one of them replied. "Ever been there?"

"No," Whitey answered.

"That's the place to be," the other said. "You've never seen a crowd until you've been there."

"Or money, either," the first brother added. "Listen, you ought to come along."

Whitey wanted to go, but he couldn't. He had nothing but the clothing he was wearing, and his outfit was dirty and ragged. In Philadelphia that did not make any difference. But Atlantic City was something else.

The brothers offered to lend Whitey the money for some new clothes. "Or a costume," they said, "if that's what you think you need."

A costume, Whitey thought. That was the answer. He didn't need new clothes. He was wearing the perfect costume. In Atlantic City he would simply tell them he was W. C. Fields, the Tramp Juggler.

He did so. And he got himself a job—with only one hitch. Between his juggling acts, young Fields had to swim out into the ocean and pretend to drown several times each day.

Whenever the crowds became too thin, Fields changed into a pair of swimming trunks. He would jump into the water and swim out to where everyone on the beach could see him. Then he was supposed to sink, float, spit out gushers of water, and kick his arms and legs about, screaming as loudly as he could for help. He was supposed to keep this up until he had attracted a large crowd on shore. Then the lifeguard, who was also paid by the manager, would swim out and halfheartedly drag Fields back to the beach.

Fields alternately juggled and drowned from early morning to late evening. From that time on, he later told people, he never took another drop of water. "I don't need to," he would snarl, screwing up his nose and looking his audience straight in the eye. "I've got it stored up like a camel. Why, I used to drown twelve times a day, seven days a week!"

Fields's next job wasn't much better. He joined up with a small, broke traveling circus that was heading for high, dry land and needed a boy about his size. It wasn't until the circus caravan and Fields were a good way down the road that he learned what his job would be. The circus's drum carrier, Fields discovered, had run off in the last town.

The next morning Fields understood why. The drum wasn't just huge and heavy; it was louder than anything he had ever heard before. Fields lugged it about for several days, trying to cover his ears and carry the deafening instrument at the same time. Before long the boy had convinced himself that if he didn't get rid of the drum soon he would never hear anything less than thunder again. Cornering the manager, he shouted something about his having come down with the beginnings of a very long and very contagious illness. "Couldn't I get my pay now," he shouted, "so I can leave here before I make everyone sick?"

The manager had heard this story before. Shaking his head, he said something Fields couldn't hear and led the boy off to another corner of the small lot. Fields had almost convinced himself that he was going to juggle again. Then he saw the elephants laughing at him.

There were three of them. Fields's job, the manager shouted in his ear, was to feed them, water them, and wash them down. And to keep from getting permanently maimed by them. They weren't mean, the manager assured Fields quickly—just full of spunk.

For several days, Fields watered the elephants. And they doused him with sprays of water from their trunks. He fed them. And they playfully bounced him back and forth between them as if he were an old volley ball.

Fields was about to slip away from the elephants—and the circus as well—when he heard that the juggler had caught the measles. Grabbing a battered silk hat from someone's prop box, an orange he had been saving for his escape, two white mice, and the ringmaster's cigar, Fields hurried into the ring.

The audience went wild. For three weeks they applauded Fields while the other juggler slowly regained his strength. When the latter was well again, the manager kept both Fields and him juggling. Fields liked the circus. He liked the ring and the crowds and the circus's air of boastful fraud. But winter came, and the circus tents were pulled down for the last time until spring. Once again Fields set out looking for work. But before he left the circus, he had a small score to settle. Late one night he took his two white mice and crept quietly to the back of the lot. There, a few feet away from the elephants' reach, he set the white mice loose.

As he later liked to tell it, Fields's next job was juggling in a dime museum in New York, which suddenly found itself with an opening when the headless lady slipped on the ice and cracked her skull. Fields moved about from one job to the next. With each position he worked himself farther away from tent shows and closer to vaudeville—and, eventually, the movies.

Fields practiced constantly. He spent night after night in his hotel room juggling whatever objects he could get his hands on. He kept tossing things around, never stopping until angry pounding from the floor below woke him up to the fact that he was half asleep and dropping everything he tossed. Exhausted, he would collapse on the bed until morning.

By the time Fields was in his late teens, his act was one of the most popular in the country. He would come on stage juggling tennis balls—and hats. One object after another would fly up into the air. Fields closed his act with a real vaudevillian flourish, balancing twenty-five cigar boxes end on end. On the top cigar box was balanced a small rubber ball. Fields would stare in dumbfounded horror at one cigar box somewhere in the middle of the pile that kept wobbling shakily, as if it were drunk. And then, while the audience watched, fascinated by what they saw, Fields would send the ball rolling off the top box and catch it in his free hand. One box after another would come tumbling down under Fields's masterful direction, without upsetting any of the others below. The audience had never seen anything like it.

When Fields was twenty, he was offered a chance to perform in Europe. He accepted, and his first show abroad was in London. On the marquee outside his theater the lights announced *The European Debut of Wm. C. Fields, The Distinguished Comedian and Greatest Juggler on Earth.* Fields, who wrote the line himself, was especially proud of the 'm' he had added to his first initial. "More dignified," he told everyone who would listen.

By this time Fields was acclaimed as the greatest juggler in the world. For years he had worked hard for that title. But once he had earned it, he became restless. He felt he could do more than juggle. He wanted to be a comedian on the stage and on the screen. He *knew* he could do it. The problem was to convince others that he could.

Everyone knew Fields was funny. All sorts of stories about him had been circulated. There was the time he was juggling hats and a huge backdrop fell with a loud racket somewhere backstage. Fields lifted his nose inquisitively and, without dropping a hat, remarked, "Mice." If anyone else had said that, it probably would not have been funny at all. But Fields could make even the alphabet sound hilarious.

Fields traveled the country from one vaudeville theater to the next. At each one he told the manager that he was a master comedian and actor, too. The managers smiled, assured him that he was a great juggler, and refused him any other job.

Fields kept traveling, juggling for any manager who would pay his price, and working his way toward Hollywood and the movie studios.

The more money Fields made with his act—and he seemed to increase his earnings every week—the more he worried about being robbed or left stranded penniless in some strange town. Wherever he went, Fields stopped at a bank and opened a savings account. He deposited ten dollars in one bank, twenty in the next—just in case he ever passed through again and needed the money. He even hopped off trains while the engine was taking on water to open another account at a bank he had spied through the window.

He opened each account under a different name—whatever he happened to make up as he stepped through the front door of the bank. At one time he carried more than seven hundred bankbooks around in one of his trunks. They were made out to such notables as Figley E. Whitesands, Sneed Hearn, and Dr. Otis Guelpe. Fields always insisted that every one of these names was real. He had seen them all somewhere, he swore. And maybe he had. It was always hard to tell whether Fields was kidding or not. Nobody enjoyed talking—and fibbing—as much as he did.

He muttered everything he said as though he did not expect his listener to believe him—and furthermore, as though he really did not care. He did care, of course. He was very concerned about what people thought of him, and he was easily offended. That was probably the reason that he played so hard at indifference.

Many of the funny things Fields did were based on his boyhood experiences. For example, he never forgot the pool sharks who hung around the poolroom where he had worked. He had watched them closely then and knew all their tricks by heart- -the serious way they chalked their cues and strutted about between shots. He thought these mannerisms were some of the funniest he had ever seen. They were funny, too, when he mimicked them.

Fields had a special pool table built. It had invisible strings to yank the balls wherever he wanted them to go. The cue he used was twisted and bent. It made his audience almost dizzy to look at it. But with one good whack, Fields was able to send all the balls careening and spinning around the table and deep into the pockets—including the one in his trousers.

Fields carried that pool table with him to Hollywood— along with several huge trunks filled with props. When he finally managed to land himself a movie role, he made good use of the props he had accumulated.

Pool Sharks, the first movie Fields ever made, was full of his tricks. There he was on the flickering screen, walking about in a bright, sunny garden, swinging a cane that somehow ended up whacking him on the head. All sorts of other catastrophes followed. He sat down on a pin, and then on a bunch of marshmallows. He managed to escape to a hammock, and as soon as he stretched out, it collapsed. Some people invited him to join them for dinner, and he ended up sitting in somebody's lap. By the time the pool game finally began, Fields had hit almost everybody and everything with his cue except the balls. The film finally ended—many disasters later—with Fields stumbling away from the wreckage.

Fields's films became so popular that he could demand and get almost anything that he wanted from Hollywood. He wrote and appeared in dozens of films. Occasionally he also directed. He asked for and was paid thousands of dollars a week—half due on Mondays, the rest on Wednesdays, as he told the studio—"Just in case there's any trouble."

Fields made a big point of examining every dollar he was paid, "Just to make sure it's not counterfeit." Fear of being swindled was probably part of the reason for his eccentric behavior. But the real one was that he enjoyed making some people nervous.

The star insisted on wearing an obviously phony clip-on moustache in many of his movies for the same reason. He insisted that the moustache was handsome and real. "All the men in my family were bearded," he would boast, "and most of the women."

The heads of the Hollywood studios swore that Fields lay awake nights figuring out ways to hound them. Fields once told a group of prominent producers that he used to be troubled with insomnia. "But now," he told them, "I've found a cure."

"What is it?" they asked, wondering if it might work for them.

"Sleep," Fields answered, setting his frayed and dented hat on his head, twirling his gold-headed cane, and stepping out the door.

Another habit that perturbed the studios was his in-

W. C. Fields

sistence on writing his own movie scripts. "It's in the contract," he would tell them. And, in fact, it was.

Fields would go home and dash off a script on the back of an old grocery list. And then he would sell it to the studio for $25,000. The next day he would give the studio a call to tell them that he'd had a good look at that script of theirs and that it was awful. "It's full of holes," he would say. "But don't worry. I'll straighten it out for you." Hanging up the phone, he would make a few important-looking scratches on the grocery list and send it back to the studio with a bill for another $25,000. When he got the money, he would toss the script aside and make up the movie as he went along.

On the movie set Fields was often an impossible person to argue with. When he was playing the part of Mr. Micawber in *David Copperfield*, he told the producer one afternoon that he thought he would like to do a bit of juggling.

"But, Mr. Fields," the producer answered, "Charles Dickens says nothing about juggling in the book."

"Hmmph. Probably forgot," Fields replied.

Money—either the lack of it or too much—always confounded Fields. In Hollywood he bought the most expensive cars he could find and then loaded them down with friends and took off on week-long picnics. But he was also known to put locks on his refrigerator. Some days he wouldn't let anyone else spend a nickel. But at other times he would sit in a restaurant all night rather than pick up the check.

A friend once found Fields dressed in an old bathrobe writing a movie script about some crazy lady who lived on a boa constrictor farm.

"What's that in your pocket?" the friend asked, seeing that an incredible roll of money was about to fall out of the robe.

"Appears to be banknotes," Fields said, pretending to be busy with his script.

"Looks like a lot," the friend said.

"It's four thousand dollars," Fields grunted.

"What's it for?" the other persisted.

"It's getaway money," Fields scowled, changing the subject.

Fields's eccentricities finally caught up with him. A doctor told him that he would have to slow down if he wanted to live more than a month longer.

"You must be a good doctor," Fields drawled. "That's exactly what a very good and very expensive specialist in Europe told me twenty-five years ago."

Unfortunately, this doctor was much closer to the truth. One of our country's most original humorists died not many weeks later. It was late in 1946, on Christmas day.

Countless boys stared in awe as Dan Rice's riverboat floated toward them through the early morning mist. Many dreamed of someday having a circus of their own—and forgot their musing as soon as the tents and the clowns had disappeared. But one morning five brothers stared at the riverboat's glow and imagined a fantasy world of red wagons and billowing white tents that was their alone. They dreamed, as all boys dream. But together John, Al, Charles, Otto, and Alfred T. Ringling made their dream come true. This is the story of the most fantastic circus the world has even seen.

The Ringling Brothers

IT'S HERE! It's here! The circus is here!" The long-awaited cry rose joyfully from the dock at McGregor, Iowa.

Later the Ringling brothers said that what surprised them most of all was not its size or its brilliant color, but the suddenness with which the circus appeared. One moment there was nothing but a few stars, and dark shadows, and the lapping of the water. And then the dawn was suddenly filled with gay circus tunes, bright lights, and laughter.

The five brothers stood still, listening, in the quiet of the early morning. There! There it came again!

From far down the river floated the unmistakable sound of a steamboat whistle. Just like all the other boys raised along the Mississippi in the 1870s, the brothers knew the sound of every steamboat that paddled past. They knew that this steamboat was special. They had never heard anything like it before. Its tune was a circus tune that grew louder and merrier the closer the steamboat came.

Others heard it, too. Excited voices whispered in the darkness. Here and there, restless figures could be seen in the glimmer of the oil lanterns that flickered along the landing.

The brothers all leaned forward, listening to the sounds. Al, sixteen and the oldest, jabbed at the fresh summer air with his finger. The others, even three-year-old John, who clung tightly to Al's other hand, stared where he pointed.

As they watched, flickering pine torches suddenly sparkled on the dark water and brightly lit the river's bend. As if out of nowhere, Dan Rice's gaily painted steamboat rounded the bend and steamed majestically ashore.

Music shook the riverbank. Five pairs of wide eyes watched every move as the steamboat and its two barges slipped to the landing. Each boy silently counted the red-and-gold chariots that crowded the barges. The brothers stared at the tent wagons, which were loaded down with enormous poles and rolls and rolls of canvas.

They nudged each other as they heard strange howls, chatterings, and roars. Squinting, their eyes searched the shadowy cages atop the flat wagons as they wondered what sorts of weird and wonderful creatures the daylight would reveal behind those hopefully sturdy bars.

As they watched, men and horses and elephants pushed and pulled the gaudy wagons onto the landing.

They watched as long as they dared. Then, reluctantly, the brothers turned and hurried back toward home and the morning's chores. As they did so, they talked about how, someday, they would have a circus of their own.

They were just boasting and dreaming. Not one of

them really believed that what they said that summer morning in 1875 would ever come true.

Believe it? They would have laughed if anyone had told them that someday the Ringling brothers would have the greatest circus in the world.

Dan Rice's circus vanished as quickly as it had come. But every bit of it, even the smell of the sawdust and animals, the popcorn and cotton candy, was kept preserved in some corner of the brothers' minds.

That summer, the brothers practiced acrobatics on a horizontal bar in their backyard. That fall they hung a trapeze from a beam in the barn. Al even learned to walk a rope he had stretched between two thick trees.

Summers came and went, and the brothers filled farm carts with tightropes and jugglers' props and then performed in the hamlets and crossroad towns that dotted the neighboring hills. And one morning in 1884 the Ringling brothers' neighbors woke, startled, to find the beginnings of a real circus right in their home town.

They listened to the rasping sound of tent poles being sawed from long logs and to the pounding sounds of benches being hammered together. Those who were curious enough stuck their heads inside the Ringlings' old barn and saw a paintbrush slapping against the side of a wagon already half-painted a bright and fiery circus red. They looked again and saw Al patching huge pieces of canvas together to make a tent, while another brother sewed bright, colorful costumes for the performers. Out behind the barn, in a dark corner of a shed, an old hyena coughed in its rickety cage.

Those who did not see the moth-eaten hyena heard about it. Everybody was discussing the colorful posters that announced the *Mammoth, Marauding, Man-Eating Monstrosity, The Hideous* Hyena Striata Gigantum [which, one of the brothers explained, was Latin for "giant striped hyena"]. *His Hideous, Blood-Curdling Laughter,* the posters boasted and warned, *Paralyzes with Terror the Bravest of Hearts.* The Ringlings' neighbors must have been exceptionally brave. For nights they lay awake listening to the old cur cough, and not one of them died of fright.

Each day the neighbors watched as more old farm wagons were pushed inside the Ringling barn to disappear until, days later, they rolled back out, brightly splashed with brilliant gold letters declaring that they, too, were part of "Yankee Robinson and Ringling Brothers' Great Double Shows, Circus and Caravan."

Everybody had heard of Yankee Robinson. For more than fifty years the old, bewhiskered trouper had thrilled audiences. He had gone from one circus to another— managing this one, owning that—until finally he had decided to let younger and more eager troupers do most of the work. And so, while the brothers worked, old Yankee sauntered about in his polished boots, ringmaster's bright red coat and top hat, spinning his tall stories for everyone who would listen to him.

Somewhere, one of the brothers found large posters illustrated with pictures of tigers. He cut them out and pasted them to the sides of the wagons. The fact that there was no tiger within a thousand miles of their circus did not bother the Ringlings. The pictures looked exciting, and excitement, they told themselves, was what a circus was all about.

Besides, they *did* have their hideous hyena, their trained horse, and an ancient dancing bear.

And there was a sideshow, too, which boasted its own tent and several curiosities, including an educated pig and a magician.

Each of the brothers did half a dozen things. And the circus had eight other performers besides themselves. A dozen wagons were needed to carry everyone and everything. Farm boys eager to see the countryside brought their horses and were hired to do the driving. Finally, the circus was ready.

The brothers gave two performances before leaving town on that special day in May. Al juggled and did a plate-spinning act. Yankee Robinson kidded the folks at the ticket counter and was the ringmaster. Young John was a clown. More than six hundred people packed the big top. So many customers came that the performers had to borrow chairs from the neighbors so that everyone could have a seat.

As soon as the second show was over, the brothers and their helpers began taking down the tents and packing everything into the wagons. It was a big job, and their audience had been home and asleep for several hours before the last of the tent poles and seats and props had been stowed away in the wagons. When the brothers finally climbed aboard their wagons and whistled to the horses to move forward, it was close to morning.

A dozen wagons creaked and groaned under their heavy loads. The kerosene lanterns that swung on the back of each wagon made a long chain of yellow light. Soon the only sounds were hoofbeats muffled in the road's thick dust, the creak of the wagons, and now and then the cough of the old hyena in its drafty cage. As the wagons disappeared over the last hill, even the drivers nodded in their sleep.

Every so often the drivers awoke. They shook their heads and kept one sleepy eye on the weather. Rain, tornadoes, and snow could cripple a show as badly as fire or accident or disease. As the wagons moved along, the drivers could see the posters that the advance men had pasted on barns and fences days before.

Each dawn the "mud show" [the name by which circus folk called their shows when they traveled by wagon] stopped alongside a river or stream. The animals were watered; the wagons were cleaned and polished. When that was all done, the costumes were taken from the trunks and put on. Then, with the horses running at full gallop, the circus rolled into the next town.

Each year the circus grew bigger, and more wagons were needed to move it. In 1890 the brothers decided it would be easier to move their show by train. Eighteen railroad cars were built especially for the Ringling brothers. Two were to travel ahead of the circus as advance cars, carrying posters and the men to paste them up in the nearby towns. The other sixteen cars made up the circus train. There was a sleeping car for the performers and one for the roustabouts. The elephants—the most valuable and pampered of all the circus beasts—had their own car. Five others carried the rest of the circus animals, and eight more were piled high with wagons and canvas and poles. The circus that year was known far and wide as "Ringling Brothers United Monster Railroad Shows, Great Triple Circus, Museum, Menagerie, Roman Hippodrome and Universal World's Exposition."

Daybreak came to city after city in 1890 as the long circus train, its silver-and-yellow sides gleaming in the early morning light, rolled to a grinding stop with one long hiss of dying steam.

Al

Alfred T.

John

Charles

Otto

Years later, when the Ringling brothers' show traveled with a hundred gaily painted railroad cars, there were four circus trains in all. The first one to arrive carried men who rushed to the deserted showgrounds to stake out the sites where each of the tents would go. The sideshows, caged animals, and cookhouse were all aboard this train, too.

The huge cookhouse, which could seat a thousand hungry people at a time, was the very first structure to go up. By that time a second engine had dragged its colorful string of cars to a halt alongside the first. It carried the poles and the rolls of canvas for the big top, and the men called roustabouts who would put up the big tents. Quickly they climbed down from the cars and lined up outside the cookhouse.

Another circus train arrived with baggage and trunks, followed by a fourth train carrying the elephants and the performers. Soon the elephants and the horses and the men were all busily working together to unload the wagons and cages from the circus flat cars.

Roustabouts and horses, wagons, elephants, tent poles, and cages of wild animals were everywhere. Two-, four-, and eight-horse teams pulled the wagons from alongside the railroad cars to the showgrounds. There as many as one thousand men worked among the huge rolls of canvas, lacing sections together. They helped to unload the giant center poles, each as tall as the mast on a clipper ship. Around the center poles, several hundred smaller poles were placed.

Burly hammer gangs swung and hammered together as if they were a single man. The elephants strained against their padded harnesses. They pulled the center poles into place and dragged the great rolls of canvas higher and higher, until—finally—the big top rose full-blown, with its flags and pennants waving over the crowded showgrounds.

Before the big top was more than a few feet off the ground, roustabouts had crawled inside, swinging the smallest poles into place and making room for the seat wagons to bring in the grandstand that would hold twelve thousand people.

By this time the circus parade was almost ready to begin. Twenty horses, decked out with red, white, and blue plumes set atop their ears, were hitched to the mammoth bandwagon. Atop it were several dozen musicians. Once the parade started, the musicians never stopped playing. The bandwagon began to move, and behind it rolled elaborate wagons of every size and shape, their frames and wheels painted gaudy circus colors, and their huge side panels carved and painted with jungle scenes. Inside these wagons, creatures from all over the world paced and snarled or lay panting upon their cages' floors. Elephants walked heavily along, trunk to tail with their neighbors, ornate blankets draped over their sides, and beautiful showgirls on their backs. At the very rear of the parade came the calliope with its merry tune.

And so it happened. The evening show followed the afternoon show, and as if by magic, the circus vanished, to appear the next morning in another city a hundred or more miles away. All through the long day and the short night, everyone moved about as if he had done whatever he was doing a thousand times before. And probably he had. Each season the circus workers took their city apart and rebuilt it more than a hundred different times.

And each spring, when the circus trains came roaring out of winter quarters, the "Biggest and Greatest Show on Earth" came closer to making its proud boast come true.

In 1917 more than three hundred horses, a dozen camels, a score of bull elephants and countless cages, bands, clowns, and floats rolled down Main Streets throughout the country in the show's spectacular parade.

The Ringling Brothers and the Barnum and Bailey circuses combined in 1919 into what became known to circus fans everywhere as "The Big One." The combined show was so huge that when it played in New York's Madison Square Garden, there was not room or time enough for all of the acts to perform.

The circus flourished throughout the 1920s. Under one enormous stretch of billowing canvas, aerialists and acrobats, bareback riders and wild animal trainers, clowns and daredevils and beautiful women performed in the bright lights. One hundred and sixty-eight exciting acts overflowed the three rings and the sawdust and even the air above. The parade was more than three miles long.

As the years went by, Al, Otto, and Alfred T. passed away. When Charles died, in 1926, John was left as the last of the original Ringling brothers. Nonetheless, the circus continued to prosper. In 1928 it featured the Great Wallendas' high wire troupe and the Flying Condonas. Hugo Zacchini, the human cannonball, joined the show for the 1929 season.

The Great Depression that gripped the nation in the early 1930s, however, seriously affected the show's income. In 1932, John Ringling lost control of the circus to a group of New York investors. The last of the brothers died in 1936. But in 1938, John Ringling North, a nephew of the brothers who had built their first big top out of scraps of canvas and poles carved from trees they had chopped down themselves, regained control of the family enterprise.

In the next decade the circus survived a number of catastrophes. Eleven elephants died in 1941 from eating grass that had been sprayed with a poisonous weed killer. Fire swept the menagerie in 1942, killing forty animals, and the musicians' union forced the circus band to quit. Another tragic fire destroyed the big top in 1944, killing 168 people. But still the circus continued as the "Biggest and Greatest Show on Earth."

Gradually, however, it became clear to even the most stubborn of circus folk that the times were changing, and the circus would have to change with them. The biggest show of all had grown *too* big. The cities that it visited had grown huge, too. Their streets were too crowded for the bright, noisy, magnificent parades on Circus Day. Empty fields had become so scarce that there seemed to be nowhere left for the huge stretches of canvas.

On a gray Monday morning in July, 1956, John Ringling North told the world that the big top was coming down for the last time. From then on, he said, the circus would play all its engagements in arenas or stadiums. It had simply become impossible for the circus to carry its own arena, generate its own power, move its thousands of seats, and feed its hundreds of workers—all in a different city every day.

There was a period of adjustment, of course. The circus was starting a new career. It changed its routing pattern, its transportation methods, and its promotional techniques —all successfully.

The fiery colored wagons and the elephants and the brass bands no longer parade down Main Street on Circus Day. The acrobats and clowns and aerialists no longer entertain beneath the huge canvas tent. But the "Ringling Brothers, Barnum and Bailey Circus" still thrives today. The dream the five brothers never forgot is still the "Big One."

Bibliography

Barnum, Phineas Taylor. *Barnum's Own Story. The Autobiography of P. T. Barnum.* New York: Dover Publications, Inc., 1961.

————. *Struggles and Triumphs: or, Forty Years' Recollections.* New York: American News Company, 1871.

Benet, Laura. *Barnum's First Circus, and Other Stories.* New York: Dodd, Mead, & Company.

Bernard, Charles. *Bernard's Half-Century Circus Review and Red Wagon Stories.* Savanna, Ill.: Commercial Lithograph and Printing Company, 1930.

Bradna, Fred, and Spence, Hartzell. *The Big Top: My Forty Years With The Greatest Show On Earth.* New York: Simon & Schuster, Inc., 1952.

Burt, Olive W. *The Ringling Brothers: Circus Boys.* New York: Bobbs-Merrill Company, Inc., 1958.

Christopher, Milbourne. *Houdini: The Untold Story.* New York: Thomas Y. Crowell, Company.

Deschner, Donald. *The Films of W. C. Fields.* New York: Citadel Press, 1966.

135

Desmond, Alice. *Barnum Presents General Tom Thumb.* 1954.

Everson, William K. *The Art of W. C. Fields.* Indianapolis: Bobbs-Merrill Company, Inc., 1967.

Fellows, Dexter William, and Freeman, Andrew A. *This Way To The Big Top.* New York: Viking Press, Inc., 1936.

Fields, W. C. *Drat! Being the Encapsulated View of Life by W. C. Fields in His Own Words.* Edited by Richard J. Anobile. New York: World Publishing Company, 1968.

Fitzsimons, Raymund. *Barnum In London.* New York: St. Martin's Press Inc., 1969.

Fox, Charles Philip. *A Ticket To The Circus.* Seattle: Superior Publishing Company, 1959.

Freeman, Larry. *Big Top Circus Days.* Watkins Glen, N.Y.: Century House, 1964.

Gibson, Walter Brown. *Houdini Magic.* Hackensack, N.J.: Wehman Brothers.

————. *Houdini's Escapes and Magic.* New York: Blue Ribbon Books, 1932.

————, and Young, Morris. *Houdini's Fabulous Magic.* Philadelphia: Chilton Book Company, 1961.

Gillette, Don Carle. *He Made Lincoln Laugh: The Story of Dan Rice.* New York: Exposition Press, 1967.

Gresham, William L. *Houdini.* New York: Macfadden Bartell Books.

————. *The Man Who Walked Through Walls.* New York: Holt, Rinehart & Winston, Inc., 1959.

Grock, Constantin d'Ernest. *Life's A Lark.* New York: Benjamin Blom, Inc., 1931.

————. *Sans Blaague.* London: Methuen & Co., Ltd., 1957.

Harlow, A. F. *Ringlings: The Wizards of the Circus.* New York: Julian Messner, Inc., 1951.

Houdini, Harry. *Houdini on Magic.* Edited by Walter Gibson and Morris Young. New York: Dover Publications, Inc., 1954.

Kendall, Lace. *Houdini: Master of Escape.* Philadelphia: Macrae Smith Co., 1960.

Kunzog, John C. "Dan Rice, Circus Man." *Bulletin of the Historical and Philosophical Society of Ohio,* vol. 15, (1957), pp. 95–116.

————. *The One-Horse Show: A Chronicle of Early Circus Days.* Jamestown, N.Y.: John C. Kunzog, 1962.

Plowden, Gene. *Those Amazing Ringlings and Their Circus.* Caldwell, Idaho: Caxton Printers, Ltd., 1967.

Ringling, Henry, and Hatch, Alden. *The Circus Kings: Our Ringling Family Story.* Garden City, N.Y.: Doubleday & Company, Inc., 1960.

Robert-Houdin, Jean Eugene. *Memoirs of Robert-Houdin, the Great Wizard, Celebrated French Conjurer, Author, and Ambassador.* Translated by R. Shelton Mackenzie. Minneapolis: C. W. Jones, 1944.

Rourke, Constance Mayfield. *Trumpets of Jubilee.* New York: Harcourt, Brace and Company, Inc., 1941.

Taylor, Robert Lewis. *W. C. Fields: His Follies and Fortunes.* Garden City, N.Y.: Doubleday & Company, Inc., 1949.

Wallace, Irving. *The Fabulous Showman: The Life and Times of P. T. Barnum.* New York: Alfred A. Knopf, Inc., 1959.

Werner, Morris Robert. *Barnum.* New York: Harcourt, Brace and Company, Inc., 1923.

Williams, Beryl, and Epstein, Samuel. *The Great Houdini: Magician Extraordinary.* New York: Julian Messner, Inc., 1950.